PRAISE FOR *A PEOPLE'S POWER*

"A riveting novel! I was on the edge of my s̶ ... A *People's Power* is a masterful story that unve̶ ... ̶ocial and environmental injustice. It will cha̶ ... ̶a have. Let it inspire and empower you!" – Maud̶ ... ̶ founder, Council of Canadians and bestselling author o̶ ... ̶nt.

"*A People's Power* tells the story of our times when corporate power and corporate greed have become threats to life and freedom. A must read for anyone who cares about the earth, people and about real democracy." – Dr. Vandana Shiva, physicist, activist and bestselling author.

"Hugo Bonjean's *A People's Power* is a work of fiction that reaches deep into the soul and reveals truths about the nature and cause of the gap between human possibility and reality far beyond the reach of nonfiction. This is not a story to be sampled or skimmed. It must be experienced page by page from beginning to end. I do not recall any book that so moved me." – David Korten, board chair, *YES! Magazine* and bestselling author of *Agenda for a New Economy* and *When Corporations Rule the World*.

"*A People's Power* is a story of corporate power and abuse, and the strength of the human spirit to rise above it. As a person who has fought a corporation for nine years all the way to the Supreme Court for justice, freedom of speech and especially freedom for farmers, reading this story was very emotional. Besides being a captivating read, this book provides the reader with an awareness of the ongoing tragedies in farming communities the world over." – Percy Schmeiser, of the documentary film *Percy Schmeiser: David versus Monsanto*, Right Livelihood Laureate, and farmer.

"*A People's Power* is a novel that winds its way through the very real events, institutions, and tragedies that make reining in corporate power and greed the most urgent priority of the 21st Century. After 20 years on the front lines in the war against corporate abuses I haven't read a story that cuts to the essence of the issues so well while touching the heart so profoundly. Read it and let it be your call to action. Together, we are A People's Power!" – Michael Marx, Executive Director, Corporate Ethics International.

"A spellbinding story of one man's quest for environmental justice while grappling with the forces of corporate greed—*A People's Power* raises powerful questions for our collective future." – Diane Dreher, Prof. of English, Santa Clara University, California and bestselling author of *The Tao of Inner Peace* and *Your Personal Renaissance*.

"*A People's Power* personalizes the saga of the corporate takeover of our food supply chain, slowly unfolding its effect on one family's destiny. Through tears of joy and grief, through chills of abhorrence and awe, I emerged from this all too real story feeling it vindicates the viewpoints, otherwise oftentimes categorized as overly idealistic or utopian, of hard-scrabble farmers and ranchers like my neighbors and myself on the edge of the prairie around Bear Butte where it is partly set. Similar to the protagonist, we refuse to accept that we are damned if we do and damned if we don't, just because our independent businesses are part of the primary sector. Every high school teacher should assign this book." – Talli Nauman, organic grower, contributing editor *Native Sun News*, Black Hills, South Dakota.

"*A People's Power* is a captivating book of a man's deep contemplation of life, compassion and justice. The story weaves together the struggles surrounding land reform, food security, eco-justice and a corporate world depriving a common man his peace of mind. *A People's Power* is timely, for it brings out the need for the world to redefine its relationship to the sacredness of Mother Earth." – Tom B.K. Goldtooth, (Dakota), Executive Director, Indigenous Environmental Network, and co-producer of the award winning documentary film, *Drumbeat for Mother Earth*.

"*A People's Power* spoke to me in many ways, as a mother, farmer and farm leader. I avidly followed David Green on his journey of discovering what is truly essential in life and how sometimes our only choices are our reactions to the events beyond our control. It echoes my life. As a family, we have sought alternatives to the current dysfunctional system and have formed relationships with other farmers and eaters to rebuild a more localized food system. We have come to the same conclusion as David Green – love, community and a close and caring relationship with the natural world around us will nurture us in ways that money cannot measure." – Joan Brady, Women's President, National Farmers Union.

"*A People's Power* is a gripping novel that explores the deep alienation and contradictions inherent in our global, capitalist, agricultural food system by recounting the dramatic dislocation of a struggling farming family confronted by these destructive forces. Bonjean presents us with a thoroughly researched, deep reflection on the need for vibrant and healthy communities with 'good, clean, and fair food.' His themes are central to the philosophy and preoccupations of the modern Slow Food movement and I would urge everyone to read this book!"
– Dr. Sinclair Philip, executive member Slow Food Canada, recipient of the Nation's Table Award from the Governor General of Canada, Co-owner of Sooke Harbour House.

"*A People's Power* sheds truth on the realities of agriculture in North America today with such simple clarity. I am a farmer and was stunned to read some of the exact conversations my husband and I have had. The despair and futility echo our own situation as farmers who were swept up in corporate bullying of 'go big or go home.' Corporate greed has stripped us of our livelihood. I'm grateful for Bonjean's gift of storytelling as it helped me to understand our farm situation a little better." – Roxanna Martens; former pork producer.

"The plot and characters of *A People's Power* reach the heart of many generations on many levels. For anyone who has taken up a cause for the community, this story will reconfirm the reason you cared."
– Frances Dover, Community leader and columnist.

"*A People's Power* is an important and timely contribution to the evolving consciousness of humanity in our collective search to design economic institutions that can function sustainably within natural laws and respect the magnificence of Mother Earth." – Alvin Manitopyes, First Nations Elder, Plains Cree/ Saulteaux Nations

"As a mother I identified with the characters in *A People's Power*. It touched my soul and took me on an emotional rollercoaster ride, from anger to laughter to heartfelt sadness. But through my tears it inspired and empowered me to act and create a better world for my child. A brilliant story!" – Melaine Sax, mother and fan.

"*A People's Power* lays bare the powerful forces that control the global economy while offering a vision of an alternative 'economy of love.' It demonstrates the amazing ability of the human spirit to overcome adversity, and to respond to the power of evil with the power of love. It stirred within me a compassion for the victims of an unjust economic system and reinforced the desperate need to work for social justice and defense of the earth." – Kurt Struckmeyer, writer and theologian, Mustard Seed School of Theology.

"*A People's Power* is a novel so real that everyone will find some part of their story in it. The various dimensions of a person's life, the ups and downs, life and death are so powerfully illustrated in this story that it undoubtedly will touch the reader's heart. Once you start reading you will not want to leave this vivid story until you finish." – Syed B. Soharwardy, Imam.

"This tale weaves a complex tapestry of relationships in a journey that explores a plethora of strategies to redress the consequences of power and seek change. Those who have been part of the struggle related to corporate agriculture will recognize the paths taken and all will see points to ponder. The surprise ending lies in the balance between violence and love." – Lorette Picciano, Executive Director, Rural Coalition/ Coalición Rural.

"As a reader not prone to the fiction genre, I found this to be a riveting novel. *A People's Power* is a spectacular read with well-rounded characters and a depth of story that engaged my intellectual side while capturing my heart. It was impossible to put the book down. Highly recommended!" – Marcie Van De Vorst, assistant manager, Chapters Polo Festival, Winnipeg.

"Hugo Bonjean writes from that place deep within that is the source of all people's power. In thought provoking fiction he calls humanity to examine the truth and consequences of our choices. Is there hope for a society that does not hold corporations responsible in the same way it does individuals? This book is a must read for anyone on the path to a more meaningful existence!" – Duane Guina, Executive Director Earthcare Connections.

"As the scientific evidence against the safety of GM food grows, *A People's Power* goes straight to the heart of the issue, focusing on the negative effect that 'toxic rescue' agriculture is having, not only on our food supply, but on individuals and communities everywhere." – Tony Marshall, organic farmer, Highwood Crossing, and recipient of Alberta's Innovation In Agriculture Award.

"Thought provoking and inspirational, *A People's Power* will give you 'food for thought' on current practices not only in agriculture and agribusiness but on the choices we make every day that influence our families, communities and our health." – Kevin Bresee, farmer.

"A heart-wrenching, yet hopeful tale, so beautifully told, that inspires us to wake up, to feel, to question our own complicity in an economic system that is a threat to life on Earth. Let this be a rallying cry that ignites our passion to protect what we love and empowers us to build a new economy that restores and serves all that we truly treasure. " – Judy Wicks, co-founder, Business Alliance for Local Living Economies (BALLE)

"A novel; a totally absorbing story that challenges the morality of the driving forces behind today's local and world economies. This is a story that will revolutionize our thinking, question our values and lead us to act in ways more appropriate for a sustainable future." – Marilyn Milavsky, social artist and community leader.

A PEOPLE'S POWER

A Novel

Hugo Bonjean

Eagle Vision Publishing

Published in March 2011 by Eagle Vision Publishing Ltd, Calgary, Alberta.
ISBN: 978-0-9737542-3-0
First printing.

For publishing information contact:
Eagle Vision Publishing A128-1600 90th Avenue S.W. Calgary, Alberta, T2V 5A8, Canada. Phone (403) 933 3913
www.apeoplespower.com
eaglevisionpublishing@gmail.com
Editors: Elizabeth Zack & Paula Kroeker
Cover & interior design: Suzanne Oel

Library and Archives Canada Cataloguing in Publication

Bonjean, Hugo, 1965-
        A people's power / Hugo Bonjean.

ISBN 978-0-9737542-3-0

        I. Title.

PS8603.O557P46 2011   C813'.6   C2011-900030-X

FOREWORD BY JULIE REMPEL

When Hugo Bonjean asked me to review his book *A People's Power* I had no idea how the story would affect me emotionally. He did say my opinion was important to him since we had lost our farm a year earlier—a farm that had been in my husband's family for generations.

Reading the story reminded me of a rant I had written while in the middle of our fight to protect our livelihood. I wanted Hugo to know how bang on he was with his story, specifically the emotional side of things. The rant that follows, I wrote on a day before we lost our farm when I started to realize where we were heading. I didn't know what else to do, so I wrote. I had never sent it to anyone before I shared it with Hugo. I simply didn't know who would want to read it or what sharing it with anyone would accomplish. I forgot I even had it until I started reading the book. I guess that day it was my way of trying to rise above everything that was getting me down.

Rant:

I don't know why I'm writing this, it may be just to talk to someone about how I feel or just because I no longer know what to do. I feel desperate. I am a mother of three beautiful children. They keep me going. I am also a wife to an amazingly patient and caring man. I am a farm wife and lately, that is the problem.

I have been, as most mothers are, the glue that tries to hold everything together. I have been less involved with the farm as I stay home to raise our young children. I am my husband's soft place to fall. I am enthusiastic and encouraging. Farming will get better, we have a bright future.

Lately, I am starting to learn some hard truths. It is affecting my ability to be encouraging and enthusiastic. I have always truly believed that money doesn't really matter. Life is more about the people you love and the matters of the heart. The reality that I am being forced to see is that money does matter. It matters a whole lot and it matters the most when you don't have it.

I also tell my children, and have believed, that your best is what you should give and it is enough. I feel like a liar when I tell my children that now. I have learned that your best is not always enough. Sometimes it falls far short.

I have been stubborn and defensive of our farming lifestyle. We were going to survive against all odds. We were going to succeed. I believed that. We diversified; we made changes and tried new things. We continue to do that. I was surging ahead confidently believing the light is at the end of the tunnel. Lately I just feel like I am in a toilet that has power flush and I cannot hang on any longer. I cannot continue to be strong. My dreams along with my identity and the things and beliefs that I have held fast to are not existent or attainable.

How long can people dream? I have always believed you need to dream, and more than that you need to believe your dreams can come true. I am fast learning that this is just another naïve "belief" that I have. It's not realistic. Not on the farm anyways. Dreams do not come true and really the best approach is to not dream because that way you won't be disappointed.

I think the thing that upsets me the most is that I am being changed. I am becoming hard. I am becoming a defeatist. I am becoming negative. It will affect my life, my relationships, and my values. I will probably rally out of this depression, but I will be changed forever. Maybe change is good?

So you may ask what affect the farm crisis is having on families. My answer to you is that it is destroying families, one person at a time, one principle at a time, one belief at a time, one dream at a time.

Maybe this year will be better.

When Hugo asked if I wanted to submit the rant as part of a foreword for his book, I was slightly uncomfortable. I confessed that while I am concerned about the global world of farming I'm not sure if I am willing to do more about it than be disgusted and feel helpless. I am a mother and at this time my main concern is our little family and our life. I know it is selfish, but it is survival. I want to be able to provide for my children in many different ways. I'm searching for some financial stability. The bottom line is that my husband and I need to explore different ways to make more money, as without it we cannot provide for our family.

Since that day of the rant I did have a new dream. I found a way to keep hope alive and surprisingly, or not, it is food orientated, proving the connection to the land is engrained deep in our bones. Maybe farmers will always be farmers at least in their heart. I now dream of providing healthy foods to people through a new company, Fresh Air Flavours. The company and the products we produce are a way for me to share my love of the outdoors and the tasty morsels that abound in the forest near my home.

I've dreamed of Fresh Air Flavours becoming successful and of how I could set up different funds that help other farm wives start businesses that give them hope and a better life. But that's not where I am today. Today I'm only taking baby steps. Today I focus on the needs of my family. I'm not sure I could go the distance of the family in this story. Although Hugo tells me I'm on the way.

While *A People's Power* is a novel, it is all too real for many farming families in the world. I felt relieved that finally someone was giving a voice to our tragedies. I also found inspiration to dream again and plow ahead. I hope that those who share my family's fate will find the same inspiration in this heartfelt story. And for those who are unaware of what is happening in farming communities in the country, I hope *A People's Power* will awaken you and inspire you to stand up for the farming families and artisans who provide food for you and your children.

Julie Rempel,   January 28, 2011

For you, the People.

A people's power is to close

A people's power is to open

A people's power is to fear

A people's power is to discover

A people's power is to control

A people's power is to flow

A people's power is to take

A people's power is to give

A people's power is to hate

A people's power is to love

A people's power is to judge

A people's power is to forgive

A people's power is to punish

A people's power is to celebrate

A people's power is to ignore

A people's power is to choose

A people's power is to destroy

A people's power is to create

A people's power is to captivate

A people's power is to liberate

A people's power is to surrender

A people's power is to resist

A people's power is to divide

A people's power is to unite

How are you using your power?

"None are more hopelessly enslaved than those who falsely believe they are free."
– Johann Wolfgang van Goethe

"The liberty of a democracy is not safe if the people tolerate the growth of private power to a point where it becomes stronger than their democratic State itself. That, in its essence, is Fascism—ownership of government by an individual, by a group, or any controlling private power."
– Franklin D. Roosevelt

"There aren't two categories of people. There aren't some that have been born to have everything, not leaving anything to the rest; and a majority that does not have anything and cannot enjoy the happiness that God has created for all. In our Christian society God wants us to share the goodness that He has given to everyone."
– Oscar Romero, Archbishop of San Salvador

x

*M*y father was a good man, despite the murders people know him for. People are not born as killers, or at least, not most of us, not my father. My father was a good man, caring, loving, with strong values; a strong, generous farmer with calloused hands, hardworking, grateful for what the land provided him.

Things are not always what they seem, and certainly not what the media likes us to believe. In the end, we are all products of our environment. Sure, we make our own decisions and determine how we deal with reality as it presents itself, and we should be accountable for that. But we don't choose what life throws at us, we don't choose all the people who cross our path, and we don't choose all the lessons along the way—lessons, experiences that determine how we respond to the challenges that are presented to us.

And when things turn bad, really bad, when one injustice follows another (or at least when we perceive it that way), when certain institutions or corporations seem to be above the law, taking away our freedom, trashing the values of equality and destroying our dreams, we all reach a point when our blood starts to boil.

But there is a point beyond, a point of no return, a point that can only be reached when all trust, all faith, in the existing structures that govern life has smoldered away. It is a point of desperation, a point beyond fear, a point beyond law. This point is also one of great clarity, courage, purpose and destiny, a point of offering—of the ultimate sacrifice for those we love and for what is most dear to us. We all know when destiny is calling!

Think about what you would be prepared to do to save your child. Think about what you would do if your life were threatened. Think about the revolution on which this great country is built.

Surely our founding fathers tried to negotiate with the King of England. They shared their perspectives on the injustice that was taking place. They tried to work within the system to create an equitable and free society. But when all diplomacy was in vain, they had to face their destiny. When they failed to see any solution within the framework of the existing laws, they took up arms, prepared to make the sacrifices that were necessary, determined to destroy the structure that enslaved them, and inspired to create a strong foundation for their dream: a society that values equality and cherishes life, liberty and the pursuit of happiness. A dream they were driven to create. A dream for which they would risk their lives. We all know when destiny is calling!

By no measure would I like to compare my father to the founding fathers of our country. His vision wasn't that grand ...or maybe it was, but he never saw his role as that important. He was a humble man of ordinary means, concerned with his crops, with an ever careful eye on the weather and the seasons. He was a man who cared for his family, a man who would give his life to keep us safe.

I, as a student of law, will soon spend my days in courtrooms where people are being judged on their actions from a particular moment in their lives. I've often wondered how a person comes to be in court, besides the consideration of their guilt or innocence. How did they get there? And now that things have struck close to home, I know there's more to the story than what sees the light of day. There's more to someone's life than the moment focused on in court, and there's always more than what the media likes us to believe.

Certainly people should be held accountable for their actions. But shouldn't we also contemplate what drives people over the edge, what drives them to a point of action that is beyond the law. Can we really, as a society, simply wipe our hands clean, or do we share in some responsibility? Is such action a sign that our structures are failing, are inadequate, or simply are not what they seem to be? Is it a sign we should get to work, adjust our laws, reshape our institutions or start with a new design altogether?

My mother did not speak a word after that day of bloodshed. It was like all life had been sucked out of her. She became a walking corpse. Her depression had started years earlier, but on that day, any last sparkle of hope, any remaining sense of emotion, any lingering memory of love, evaporated. A year later, to the day, she took her own life.

I never understood exactly what happened on that day in the spring, not until I started asking questions and talked to people who had known my father, not until I came to understand my father's challenges and perspectives on the world, not until I examined the events that led up to that day when our family ceased to exist, and not until my mother's death.

Now, three years after the events, I could tell you my father's story, the real story, but would you believe me? After all, I am my father's daughter, a killer's daughter. I might be biased or have an interest in changing the truth—putting things on the shoulders of a mighty corporation to justify what happened, giving my father an excuse, making him look better than he really was. So instead, I'm going to present you with the newspaper articles, the diary excerpts, and the accounts of the people I talked to so you can form your own opinion and come to your own conclusions.

Things aren't always as they seem. My father was a good man!

A WYOMING NEWSPAPER, MAY 18TH, 2007.

Empuro Inc. decapitated: top management brutally murdered during executive retreat.

Yesterday morning a disgruntled farmer walked into an off-site conference room at the Whispering Stones Guest Ranch and Conference Center at the foot of the Big Horn Mountains near Sheridan and shot Empuro Inc.'s CEO and seven executive vice-presidents with a shotgun before being shot by police after resisting arrest upon leaving the premises.

David Green, a forty-eight-year-old farmer from Wyoming who two years ago lost a court case against the biotechnology company, drove his old pick-up truck to the ranch which often hosts executive retreats in a small private five-star facility located some distance from the main ranch building and killed all those present in the meeting room with his shotgun. The ranch owners immediately called the police upon hearing the shots. Green stayed in the building until the police had surrounded the premises. Then he walked out, loaded and aimed his gun at the officers before he was shot in the chest. He died of his wounds on site.

No other people were in the building when the shooting took place. The presenter who was hired by the corporation escaped the slaying by arriving late.

"He had it in for those people, not for anyone else on the ranch," said Phyllis Wills, the owner of the ranch. "As soon as I stepped out of the ranch house onto the driveway to see what was going on at the retreat cabin, he opened the door and fired in the air. Then he went back inside. I saw one vehicle leave the property. The gunman was chasing off everyone who approached the meeting room until the police arrived."

"It seemed that he didn't want to get away," said Police Chief Matthews. "When he threatened to fire at us we had no other choice but to return fire. He knew he had no chance. It was an obvious suicide mission."

The victims were identified as Walter Simpson, 58, CEO of the company; Dale Daltier, 54, COO; Rick Monarch, 48, Executive Vice-President of Marketing and Sales; Lynn Wilcox, 55, Executive Vice-President of Research and Development; Matthew Shanagan, 53, Executive Vice-President and Legal Counsel; Kurt Fisher, 58, Executive Vice-President of Finance; and Andrew Farrett, 46, Executive Vice-President of Human Resources. All were declared dead at the scene.

Mrs. Wills added, "People come here because it is so quiet and peaceful. How could such a tragedy happen here? My prayers are with the families and friends of the people who died today."

KRISTEN SMITH, 39, ENVIRONMENTALIST.

I loved him . . . still do . . . always will. David and I had something special. It was like we were soul mates, and had always been together, not only in this life, but before this life as well. He could feel my pain when my heart was aching. He could sense my confusion when my mind was filled with fear for sharing my feelings of love—a love that was never rational, predictable or at peace. And he could guide my passion into a focused drive, like a horse whisperer connects with the soul—the essence of our being—taming the wild horses inside of me.

David loved his wife deeply despite her ongoing battle with depression. He was a man of his word; he had pledged his love in marriage, and was going to stand by his woman until his last breath. But he also honored me by being open about our relationship even when others disapproved.

"Why is it so difficult for people to accept that we can love more than one person?" he asked me once on one of our strolls along the creek. "We all have the capacity to love all of our children. So why can we not love more than one adult? Sure, each relationship is different, just like we love our children uniquely because of who they are. People love their brothers and sisters and other family members all at the same time. So how could anyone conclude that my love for you violates my love for my wife?"

David was special, not because of what he had achieved, but because of who he was. He was a man of action; he didn't believe in too much talk, and he hated diplomacy. "Things would be so much easier if people would just say what they want to say and if we all would accept that each person has the right to their personal opinions and feelings," he said. "But most of us assume people tell us things to break us down, instead of welcoming a growth opportunity with every word of feedback we encounter in life."

David dared to dream bold, undeterred by the sheer magnitude of the vision of a better world. He wanted to make a difference, to leave this world a better place. But he didn't believe in protests, at least not when I first met him. "When a pest is invading my crop, it won't help to complain," he said. "I'll only get a harvest by acting and removing the root cause, by killing the pest!"

David never gave up hope despite the blows life dealt him. Like most farmers, he was a man of patience; prepared to wait until the soil is fertile before sowing, prepared to wait until discovering a problem's root cause before acting, and prepared to wait for the enemy to show a weakness before striking.

David dreamed of a true democratic society, a country where people not only talk of equality, freedom and the pursuit of happiness, but where they shape such reality every day. Over the years, the injustices and pains he experienced all pointed to one pest: corporate power. To him, it was the root cause of all the wrongs in the world. It was the pinnacle of human ignorance and stupidity and the barrier to a just and sustainable world. And he was determined to strike at its heart.

Most people might think of him differently. But I tell you David was not a killer: he was a farmer, a creator, and a realist. He reminded me often that creation and destruction are two sides of the same coin. "For something to live, something else has to die," he said. David believed in a different world than the world we see around us today. He believed in a world where people care for each other, respect all life on the planet and live in harmony with their surroundings. For that dream to be born, the old dream of power, control and greed had to die.

David was a good man ...even though that might be difficult to understand after what has happened. His dream and his unwavering hope inspired me, and many others who knew him. The vision lives on. I loved David with my entire heart and soul . . . still do . . . always will.

TIM BENNETT, 51, FRIEND, BUSINESSMAN.

We were born a week apart. David was the oldest. Our mothers were best friends living next door to each other. Now, don't imagine that we could shout over the fence or something. "Next door" where we came from meant that you could see each other's farmhouses in the distance.

People think Saskatchewan is just flat and boring. It's true that in places it is flat, but in most areas there's a soft glow to the land so that from a small rise you can see miles in every direction. And our childhood was all but boring. Farm fields, creeks, barns, horses, chickens and sleds; it was a playground without limits.

In those days, the homesteads were still within eyesight of each other. There was nothing industrial about farming yet, although we did have tractors. Farming was still an honorable job back then. Not to say that it isn't honorable today, it's just that it was more respected or something. It was a livelihood and a lifestyle. Farmers were connected with the land. They observed the sky, the sun, the animals and the plants to predict the weather, and they discussed their forecasts whenever they got together. They had a connection with the seeds they sowed, the plants they nurtured and the crops they harvested. And they respected the soil; they could judge the quality of a piece of land by digging their hands into a chunk of dirt and crumbling it between their fingers as they judged soil density, water retention and the smell of aged organic matter. They welcomed the earthworms for the important work they did, and always had an appreciation for those important pollinators like bees and other flying insects; without those critters nothing would grow at all. A farmer back then would stand tall in his fields and take pride in what he did: feeding the world. He provided people with their breakfast, lunch and dinner.

All that being said, it doesn't mean that farmers don't take pride in their work today, or are any less knowledgeable. But they do seem to be more connected with their machinery, which now farms tracts of land well beyond the horizon, and with the genetically modified or hybrid seeds they buy annually from the seed companies.

I just wonder though how much pride the farmers of today still take in providing people with their daily food, how much connection they still have with the land. They see the declining villages whenever they go into town. They have to drive further and further to bring their children to school, buy their groceries, deliver their crops or livestock, or meet with neighbors and friends. For decades their very communities have been under attack. As family farms are squeezed out by the move to industrial agriculture, village life breaks down and people are forced to settle in large cities in search of jobs. You only have to drive through Saskatchewan, or any other farming area in North America, to witness the boarded-up, paint-weathered farmhouses with doors not opened in decades and rusted, broken-down vehicles in the yard. If those houses could only tell their stories! They are like ghosts of a time long gone, left behind as memory markers for some, and seeds of imagination for most. Can you tell I miss those days?

But you didn't come here for a history lesson on farming—although to understand David, you have to understand what farmers have gone through over the past fifty years. What farmers endured disgraced many families and turned good men, hard-working men, into either serfs of big corporations—and often enemies of their neighbors—or into broken souls, shadows of their former selves in search of just any job in the city and laden with the guilt of failure and the everlasting longing for the land and whispers of a lifestyle long gone. Men crushed by incomprehensible economic forces—forces that resemble robbery more than the free market principles people always talk about.

David and I took different paths through life, although we did end up somewhat in the same place. I chose corporate serfdom and rose to the top, or so I thought. David chose the difficult road and demonstrated to us all that there is another way. He chose to defy the entire system—even though he did try to comply for a while and paid a gruesome price for that.

Life wasn't easy on him. David didn't just get one whack of the hammer; he was beaten by hardship over and over again. Any other man would have broken down under such trials, but not David. I've never known anyone with such strong spirit, such faith and endurance, and the ability to appreciate the good things in life, even in times of darkness.

When I heard about what happened, I was dumbfounded. Not because of what had happened, as there was some justice in it given all the broken families and farmer suicides caused by the actions of those men in their pursuit of power and wealth. Not because someone snapped and went berserk with a shotgun—that seems to happen more and more in a world where true community evaporates, families break down and people have to fend for themselves every day in a musical-chairs economy.

What was so shocking to me was that it was *David*. The man who always appreciated the sunrise, the man who loved life even when it was hard, the man who forgave and moved on, the man who was shaping a vision for the world based on love, the man who was always there for his family and friends and never lost his temper. Even to this day, I cannot fathom David wielding a gun like a cold-blooded killer. It's not the man I knew.

It's not what I will remember. I wasn't there on that tragic day. Life can do strange things to people. But I'm going to remember

David for the good times we had together, even though we had a fallout that lasted decades.

There was a time when David and I saw things very differently, but in the end, I am the man I am today because of my neighbor friend, whom I lost and then found again. I choose to remember David for the vision of love that found root in his bruised soul and for the bright, inspiring and honest person he was—a man bigger than life itself, indestructible, most caring and compassionate with a heart of love.

LISA FLANN, 20, PSYCHOLOGY STUDENT.

I cried for days. I cried for David's death. I cried for the death of the men and women at that executive retreat, for their families, their spouses and their children. I cried for my loss of a trusted coach. And I cried for my confusion, for not being able to make sense of the world, for the important life lessons David taught me—lessons that were betrayed by him, yet still valuable and insightful. But somehow I felt I had to let them go, throw them out, abandon that wisdom, a wisdom so important but now stained with blood.

I remember when David presented a program at Sheridan High School when I was in eleventh grade. We thought his accent was funny, like the way he said "eh" at the end of every sentence. He had grown up in Canada and had lived in South Dakota before moving to Wyoming. He had a small organic farm just west of Sheridan, near Clearmont. "My one acre food paradise," he jokingly called it.

David had lost his son and wanted to share with us what he had learned in life; the things that sustained him and still made him appreciate each day. He felt that sharing those insights gave purpose to his son's death, but also to his own life. "In return," he said, "I receive a spark of that teenage vitality and zest for life you guys and girls still have." It was something he enjoyed being around, something he had lost when his son died.

The program consisted of some thirty hours of after-school time and was open to juniors and seniors. David contributed his volunteer time. In return we, the students, had to organize a fundraiser for a charity of our choice—on top of the thirty hours of after-school classes. We always had the option to drop out if we didn't like what we were learning. The group was limited to a dozen students, based on a first-come, first-served basis.

I'm not sure what it was that attracted me to the program. Maybe it was mere curiosity to find out why a stranger would spend some of his free time with a group of unknown teenagers. Maybe it was to find out how such a farmer, built like a wrestling champ and scarred by the death of his child, could be so soft-spoken, be at peace and have this aura of gratefulness. Or maybe it was simply to make sure that I didn't miss out on anything.

When I attended the first meeting I only went to check it out. No real expectations, no real plans to stay through the entire program. Just wanted to find out what drove me to be there.

I returned to school at six p.m., nervous, not because of the program or because of the coach, but because I was afraid some of my classmates might see me and consider me a nerd. After all, who would want to spend more time in school than you had to? None of us had really talked about attending the program, so I wasn't sure who would show up. I was also afraid I would be the only one.

When I arrived at the school, the hallway was marked with yellow paper arrows which read "life lessons." Rather than directing me to a classroom, they led me to the school library. I was late, intentionally. I figured if I was the only one there, I could silently sneak out. Surprised but relieved, I spied nine of my classmates; one was my best friend. I guess none of us wanted to be seen as nerds.

They were all hanging out on cushions on the floor and were watching a movie . . . and David, he was hanging out with them! He smiled at me when I entered, and invited me to find a place and enjoy the movie. No reprimand for being late, no sign of frustration or gaze of disapproval. Friendly and welcoming, like being late was totally normal and acceptable.

We watched *Dead Poets Society*, a story about a boy who commits suicide when he can't handle the pressures of the world around him, but also a story about the importance of seizing the day, of being grateful for the life we have and consciously choosing what our verse will be in the great play of life on earth.

"A particularly hard story for someone who's lost a son," I thought.

Where I was expecting a lecture that evening, we didn't get one, but rather left with more questions than we had when we arrived. Where I questioned my sanity for spending even more time in school, I found the time had flown by.

We left the school shortly after ten that night with a thirst for more. David had used the movie to start a discussion about responsibility, life and the purpose of it. Why are we here? What do we want to achieve? What holds us back? Which fears stop us from reaching for our dreams? Are we taking responsibility for what we do? Do we learn from our actions, from what life is teaching us? To what extent are we all a product of our environment . . . and does that leave any responsibility to that environment? Are we grateful for what we are given, for life itself? And how do we deal with life when it presents a challenge, when it presents itself in a way we would at first sight consider unexpected or undesirable?

When I heard on the news about the tragic event, those incomprehensible killings, I had to think about that first night in the library—the calmness of that strong man, undisturbed by my tardiness, and his welcoming smile. I had to think about the contrast between the events described and the man I had known.

From reading the media articles, David did something horrible, but I've known him as a wise man whose love of life could not be contained by this world. He shared stories and coached us on finding our own answers to questions I never would have asked. Questions about the origin of things—often commonsense questions, the kind no one seems to ask these days.

"We are so focused on the 'what' and the 'how,'" he said, "but we should be asking the often more fundamental question of 'why?' since the 'why' often makes the 'what' and the 'how' redundant."

The media reported on the tragic events of that dreadful day by answering the 'what' and the 'how' as they always do. The question that lingers in my mind though, is 'why?' Why did this happen? Why do some people break down and do such horrible things? Why do good people do bad things?

JOHN HOWARD, 56, RETIRED FBI AGENT.

Sometimes the people we think we know best hide the biggest secrets. They can be the exemplary husbands, the loving fathers, the excelling businessmen, the humble farmers or the engaged community members. But they have a shadow side dark as death, conspiring and rebellious but also controlled, calm, calculated and focused.

Their shadow provides them the moral authority to act according to their own set of laws, to do as they see fit, justifying their means, whatever they are, to reach their envisioned goals. They trample the law, are inconsiderate of the harm they inflict on others and have the pretension to take silent pride in achieving their objectives.

Many such men have a shadow side driven by greed, but the most ominous villains of darkness are rebels: rebels with a cause, rebels who entitle themselves to act as they please, rob in the name of the poor, conspire to overthrow governments and kill as they see fit—all in the name of the common good and creating a better world. These are men whom no one would expect to be involved in any such thing.

Those who surround such men speak well of them, and even admire them. Little do they know what drives their kindness, their seemingly giving nature and exemplary behavior! But all of it is pure calculated drama, perfectly executed; a well-planned cover for their true nature: evil. David was such a man!

You want to know if this shooting was a surprise to me? I guess it was, otherwise we—the FBI—would have prevented it. But what was no surprise was that David had a dark side, one clearly of a violent nature. Don't just believe those who claim to have known him. I tell you, the man had a shadow side and he was a master of building his cover. He was a member of a most secretive organization which we detected in 2004. And for the four years he belonged to this organization, hardly any of his friends or family had any idea about it. That alone is enough proof; David had a shadow side.

It's astounding to me that people still defend him and won't recognize what he really was, a cold-blooded killer. The only silver lining was that he refused to give up his gun. Justice was done. He got what he deserved. At least he won't kill anyone else.

FATHER JACK MARSHAL, 62, PASTOR.

I immediately noticed David and his wife, Jody, during the Sunday service. As a responsible community pastor, I'm of course supposed to notice any newcomers in our church, and given how small a church we have here in Clearmont, I do. But I would have noticed David as a newcomer in a crowd of thousands. He stood like a rock in the current, strong yet with the gentlest heart. His eyes spoke of wisdom and determination, but also of love and compassion; his soul strong with hardships encountered and brightened by spiritual wisdom discovered along the way.

But in the end, even the strongest rocks and most loving hearts are swallowed by the current. Praise Jesus! The Lord's own Son set such an example in life and was crucified by the mob. And look at the church that grew from that, a church built on His life and death.

David was a good Christian. You might be surprised by my saying that after what he did. He certainly was no saint, but he had a good heart. I know they say he killed those people in cold blood; I guess the devil must have taken possession of him, because David was a good man. He loved life, and defended it at all cost. I cannot imagine him as a heartless killer.

He was a hunter who shot quite a few deer and elk in his life, but always with respect. He always prayed before a hunt and expressed his gratitude when he was offered a life.

He must have been possessed that day. He wasn't the kind of person who would justify the brutal killings of those executives. No matter what they did. He always said, "We are here to do, not to judge. Judgment is up to the Lord." And so David would follow whatever his heart told him to do, a heart filled with love and compassion.

He must have been possessed that day!

You must know . . . he was a good Christian, but not an ordinary one. He actually never referred to himself as a "Christian."

I asked him once why he attended my church. He said, "Father, I'm here because this is Holy ground. You have the only church in town. No offense, but any Holy ground (he meant, 'any church') would do for me. I'm here because I enjoy communicating with God in community once a week. But I talk to Him daily. He is in my fields, in the soil and the sun, among the birds and the bees, and He speaks to me."

David was a man of faith, but one who took responsibility and control over his own faith. When he talked to me about God, once in a while he'd refer to Him as "Her," or as "the Divine," or as "Great Spirit." To David they were all the same; it didn't matter to him how we addressed God.

In truth, he broadened my own perspective, my spiritual understanding. Not that he would ever lay claim to such a thing—he was far too humble for that—but he did. I thank God for putting this man on my path through life. He taught me to be less judgmental, to keep an open heart towards all people just like Jesus did, no matter their background, their religion or spiritual path.

I will always remember the profoundness of some of his insights. Like one day when I questioned him on why he would not call himself a Christian. He said, "Father, labels divide! By taking on a label I judge myself. And taking on a religious label often means we judge ourselves to be better than people who don't take up that label."

"But what's so wrong with declaring that you are a follower of Jesus?" I asked.

"Father," he said, "it's by eating from the tree of judgment that we fall from the Garden of Eden. I simply decided to return to Eden. It's much easier to appreciate life and be grateful for what we have and for the people we encounter once we stop judging. I'll leave the judging up to God. And I'm sure He'll judge me by my actions instead of by my label, or by the path I follow to communicate with Him . . . or Her."

He pondered a while and then continued, "I'm not even sure if He judges at all. Why would He have given us free will? There's so much we don't know. What I do know is that through prayer and listening to my heart, I can communicate with God. And your words every Sunday, just like the words of all spiritual men and women across the world, make me reflect on life. Reflection leads to compassion, and I believe that compassion allows me to be a better person and to better understand both the world and God."

David would attend church every Sunday. He knew the Bible and the scriptures well. His understanding went beyond the words to the true meaning and the intention of what was written.

He must have been possessed that day.

He had this friend, this Native elder; Soaring Eagle was his name. They often went together to the mountains. I never met his friend until David's funeral. He was one of the few people to attend. I hope Soaring Eagle didn't open a way for Satan to take a hold of

David's soul through his tribe's heathen practices. No, that can't be. That's how I would have thought years ago, before David came into my life.

David shared with me the things he learned from Soaring Eagle, and he challenged me to find the similarities with the scriptures. He showed me how oftentimes the spiritual teachings from Soaring Eagle gave deeper meaning to the words of the scriptures. It's true—and even the scriptures say it—learning from nature is like learning from God's actions instead of from His words. Words can be misinterpreted. Actions are truth. Then why would it be surprising that indigenous spiritual paths based on God's display around them lead to truth, to love and to God? It is written in Logion 77: "I am the Light that is above them all. I am the All; the All came forth from Me and the All attained to Me. Cleave a piece of wood, I am there; lift up the stone and you will find Me there."

We are all too small to understand God's plan. As David said, it's not up to us to figure that out, or to judge the world around us, but rather to follow our hearts, build compassion and spread our love. I'm sure God had His reasons for what happened on that tragic day.

My prayers are with David and all those who died, and with their families. May those left behind find the same strength David found in the wake of his son's death. May they learn to appreciate the sunrise again and be grateful for the lives of those who crossed their paths.

Soaring Eagle, Age Unknown, Lakota Elder.

David was a dreamer. He tried to kill his dream when tragedy struck the first time. He went in search of a new dream when tragedy struck a second time. When tragedy struck a third time he realized that life and death are parts of the same dream. Darkness and light are merely flipsides of the same reality; both are needed for the Sacred Hoop to keep spinning. In order for new life to germinate, an old life has to terminate. In order for a new dream to germinate, an old dream has to terminate.

In the last phase of his life David had accepted the sacrifice for the dream. He had called his farm "Crazy Horse Fields" in honor of our brave Lakota warrior and with the hope that his spirit might be touched by our ancestor. David was a brave warrior; he lived his dream, struggled for it, made the highest sacrifice for it, and will be honored for it. Crazy Horse might have heard and answered his prayers.

Eva Green, 73, David's Mother.

Don't you believe a word of what you read in the newspapers! I know they wrote some horrible things about my David. But don't you believe it! He just happened to be in the wrong place at the wrong time with a gun in his hands and they shot him, the bastards! No investigation, no trial, not even a question! Don't you believe what they say about him! He was a good boy, a Christian, a hardworking farmer with respect for life and God's creation.

Those men they claim he killed; they all had blood on their hands. Not just that of Tom . . . my grandson . . . David's son, but of entire communities affected by their greed-driven criminal business practices. They got what they deserved! I know that sounds cruel, but it's no less cruel than what they did. I'm no saint. I go to church and try to live a righteous life, but I've never been able to forgive them for what they did to our Tom. But where do you read about that story? Where do you see any of that justice written?

We once had a teenage boy in the community who in his young invincible naivety lost control of his car on a wet road on a spring day. He hit a twelve-year-old girl, and the poor child died on the scene. It broke the young fellow's heart. He couldn't understand why God had not taken him. Guilt-ridden, he felt he had no right to live. He sought forgiveness from the girl's parents when the pain was still fresh and their tears hadn't stopped flowing. God bless those people for having the courage and the wisdom during that hour of darkness to understand that even though one life was gone, a second was in the balance. And so they mustered it together to forgive the teenage boy. The community gathered around both families with food, compassion and support. At the girl's funeral both families mourned together surrounded by the entire community.

But as the community was surrounding those who were hurt with care and support, the vultures arrived as well. Armed with cameras and microphones they came attracted by the smell of blood, a smell their crowd feeds on, just like the spectators at Rome's coliseum two thousand years ago. Their main purpose, of course, wasn't to report on the facts, nor was it to report on the story of how a community pulled together in a time of tragedy. Their only interest was to find out who they could blame, crucify and feed to the mob which was eagerly waiting, stones in hand, to cast their judgment.

A police investigation was ongoing to piece together the many variables that had been at play that morning. But who cares about thorough investigation these days?! The mob wanted blood; to know where to throw their stones. And this was an obvious case: a teenager was involved. Teenagers, the embarrassment of society, the villains— or so they are treated all too often—instead of the young adults they are, young people in search of identity, trying to carve out their space in an ever more confused world. Why is it we forget so fast how important those years were for every one of us?

And so in their desperate search for blood the media skillfully created a horrifying story about a reckless teen whose contempt for rules and other people in society led to the brutal killing of a poor child. The mob was content with the bone they were thrown, and eagerly filled in the blanks. And around the country, in any place where people gathered, everywhere but in this community, the teenager got crucified.

The media representatives could have reported on the strength of the girl's parents in forgiving the teenager. They could have reported on how such accidental circumstances often forever mark the lives of those who cause the suffering, or they could have reported on how a community pulled together in a time of mourning. But there was no excitement in such a story, there were no stones to cast and most importantly, there was no blood in it. Don't you believe a word of what you read in the newspapers!

Nowadays the media is not just in bed with big business, it's owned by the same robber barons. Things used to be different. There was a time when we could rely on the news. Journalists and newsmen saw it as their duty to inform the public and protect our democracy from those who are trying to steal it away right from under our noses.

I might not see all that well anymore at my age, but I'm no dummy, you know. It all still works pretty well up here. And I tell you, this world is going to pieces. It's being driven off a cliff by men in suits. They claim to be guided by the free market, but they are the first to shackle the freedom of entrepreneurs. They claim their technology and new laboratory seeds benefit humanity, but in truth they only benefit their pocketbooks. They claim their chemicals, packaging and products improve our lifestyles, but in truth they create dependence and serfdom, giving them ever more control over our lives.

They are smart! Instead of fighting independent media companies, they either bought them or killed them, and now they create the stories they want us to swallow from media channels they own.

But a mother knows her children. I know my David, and I tell you he didn't kill anyone!

I remember the day he was born like it was yesterday. He was our first and only child. I was twenty-four. David was born two weeks early when my husband and I were attending the wedding of one of his best friends in Bismarck, North Dakota. The doctor had given his blessings for the short trip; it was only a few hours by car, and we would return the following day. But right when we got there, my water broke and I went into labor for sixteen hours. As I neared exhaustion David finally decided to leave my womb and enter this world. The doctor grabbed him by one leg. He lifted him upside down, and the first thing my little David did was pee on me. That was his first statement in life, and he never really changed. He was a most loving child, but David had no respect for authority and rules if they didn't make any sense. He was his own man, and the people who crossed his path would quickly figure that out. Not that he was aggressive about it—on the contrary, he was always calm and collected—but stubborn and determined. His actions always spoke louder than his words.

They say kids mimic their mother or father. And granted, I do believe we have an influence. But I'm convinced we are all born as our own person, as an independent soul with our own path and purpose, and no parent is going to change that.

My David was born with such purpose, in his case an intense sense of justice. He couldn't stand by and let an injustice go unchallenged. I only realized how deep this passion for justice was rooted when he was nine. One day, one of his fellow classmates accused him of having stolen his milk. Deeply insulted for such an unjust and groundless claim he defended himself, but then his teacher questioned him on the same thing. Angry because he expected his teacher to know his integrity, he left school and biked home. With tears in his eyes he related the story to me. I knew he hadn't stolen the milk. So I asked him more as a confirmation than as an accusation, "And you didn't steal the milk, right?" My words weren't cold yet, and I saw how something broke in his eyes. His expression was one of disbelief and deep pain. The tears he had bravely held back when telling me the story started to roll down his face. He turned around and left the house. I followed him to the porch and saw him bike down the driveway. I assumed he would head to the neighboring farm, to see his best friend, Tim, when he arrived from school. So I turned back to my cooking.

Around suppertime I phoned Tim's mother to ask her to send David home. When I learned he wasn't there, I panicked. It was already getting dark and I had no idea where my nine-year-old son had gone. By nine that night, I had lost it and could hardly wait for my husband to return—God rest his soul. He had gone to town in the morning, and usually took the time to connect with some friends and visit his parents before returning home. At around ten o'clock the engine of our old pick-up truck announced my husband's arrival. I stormed outside, but was stopped in my tracks when I saw my husband approach, his hand on David's shoulder.

"Daddy believed me!" David shot out, eyes like fire.

I turned around and walked back into the kitchen, fuming with anger, but also relieved to have my son back. David had ridden his little bicycle for some three hours through farm fields and then navigated through town to my husband's parents' house to explain to his dad how unfairly he had been treated at school and that I hadn't believed him.

David also had an unexplainably deep connection with indigenous people from around the world, and specifically the First Nations people here in Canada. Not that he knew so many or even hung out with them all that often. But there was this one Native boy in his class. One year, David must have been fourteen or fifteen when some children at the local rodeo were making fun of the Indian boy's long braids. And suddenly, my little David, who was always so collected, calm and compassionate, went into a rage and grabbed a boy almost twice his size by the throat and hissed with the earnestness of a viper ready to strike, "Leave my friend alone, or I'll kill you!" Of course he didn't mean that, but that's how foolish youngsters can act when their anger takes control of them. The strange thing was this native boy wasn't even part of David's circle of friends.

Lucky we parents were around and could pull the two young hotheads apart before things got out of hand. David would have been no match for the boy, but his fierceness and the power in his eyes had completely disarmed the other young man.

I remembered the prior week David had watched this movie about the slaughter at Wounded Knee, and I had noticed how quiet and introspective he had been during the days that followed. David didn't share his emotions easily, and chose to endure his pain and joys mostly in silence.

When I questioned him about this sudden outburst of aggression, something he had never displayed before, or ever since, he said, "You know that movie I watched last week. I could feel their pain. It was like I had been there; had seen the slaughter firsthand. They were my children, my wife, my parents and my grandparents that were massacred there."

I could see the pain in his eyes. His soul was hurting and his heart torn apart by the senseless brutal killing, the disrespect for life and the injustice done. Before I could tell him not to take movies too seriously, he continued, "I picked up a book at the school library about the history of the Wounded Knee massacre to understand what truly happened. Even though the boys today might not have realized what they were doing, the massacre hasn't ended."

Then he looked me straight in the eyes and with determination in his voice said, "And it's got to stop! It has to be stopped!"

I knew then there is more to a person than what he receives from his parents. There is a uniqueness and a history to each soul, and as parents we're only here to coach it and set it on its way. But the soul will follow its own path; nothing we do as parents will change that. We can only hope to help our children build a toolkit, offer alternative perspectives, and challenge their choices, in order to support the inevitable journey the soul has to make.

David wasn't an easy child, but he was a good child. His principles and his sense of righteousness were paramount to him. They were oftentimes more important to him than people, which led to pain in his life as friendships crashed like ships carried by the surge onto the rocks before the shore. David and Tim were inseparable as children, but I noticed how David's uncompromising values were causing a rift in their relationship during their last year in high school.

Tim Bennett, Friend, Businessman.

Grade twelve was a tough year for all of us. Up till that time, life was fairly stress-free—like for all teenagers—even though at that age we didn't think so. We all felt the tension rising during that last year of high school as the end of our worry-free existence came in sight. Not only was a chapter closing on an amazing part of our life, but we also had to choose what we were going to do with our future. How were we going to make a contribution to this world? What job would we enjoy and be good at?

How were we supposed to know? What if we made the wrong choice? On top of all that we knew we would all go our own ways, something we avoided talking about like the plague. All the incredible friendships that had sustained us through our youth would grow stale and vaporize. So we cherished our time and increased the number of parties and camping trips, all in a desperate attempt to create a lasting memory of something that the inevitability of time would steal away from us—an experience we all yearned to hang on to.

David and I had been inseparable throughout our childhood, but lately there was a tension lurking between us. More and more during class debates on social issues we'd find ourselves fiercely defending opposite positions.

That last year of high school our class participated in a model United Nations conference. It was a hands-on and entertaining way to

give us an understanding of the larger issues in the world. Different
student groups enacted a dialogue on bridging the divide between the
first and third world countries. David and I were in opposing camps.
His group represented Chile; mine, the United States of America.

In a passionate effort David was able to unite all developing
countries of the conference so they spoke with one voice. Despite
such an unusual alliance, they still couldn't achieve their objectives of
economic independence and poverty alleviation without giving up
some crucial points of their agenda. The simple fact was, they needed
capital and that capital was concentrated in the first world countries—
or, as David would say, "The countries where most of the super-class
resides." The reality was that globalization and world trade
agreements had chained the independent sovereignty of nations.
David rebelled against that reality. He argued, "When a people lose
control over their own resources due to some one-sided international
trade agreements, then who really controls their country . . . and
what then is the true value of democracy?"

The conference was like a game of Monopoly, where the
assets to be traded were a country's resources. And within that game
of horse trading, money and the operation of markets defined what
was good for people—or at least, that's what we were being taught.
After all, that's how the real world works today.

But David challenged that status quo. He asked, "Why is
there no room for compassion, fairness and empathy, let alone
responsibility for historic actions? Why is there no room to consider
the consequences of our actions on the environment and on other
people? And why do we blindly trust that the markets, when left
alone, will raise all boats in a rising tide when there is no proof of
that?"

His last question hit on a convenient myth that allowed those in power to stay in power. Not only did it prevent their actions from being challenged, even better, it provided a moral justification for their actions. It presented them as exemplary behavior, carried out for the good of all. In my young ignorance I bought into the myth; it was only years later after a successful business career that I finally woke up to reality.

David, on the other hand, saw the scam for what it was right from the start.

We had a heated discussion when the event was over. I tried to explain that it was only a mock conference, and that we won fair and square following the rules of the game.

David snapped in response, "And why did you find it necessary to follow the rules? This was our opportunity to reshape the world, to show how things could be done differently, rewrite the rules and create a better world. Who cares about reality and the current rules of the game?"

When he continued, it was the heartbroken tone in his voice that made me realize how seriously David had taken this event and how profound his disappointment in me was. He said, "We had a chance here to rewrite reality, to demonstrate how our generation will do things differently. We had a chance to show how we plan to write a new reality for the future. How could you have failed to grasp that?"

And so our differences grew. I couldn't really understand why David had such a problem with the way I saw things. After all, I was only embracing the ways of the world; I understood that money ruled this world and provided opportunities. The family farms around us were under stress and disappearing as farmer after farmer declared bankruptcy and moved to the city in search of work. I had decided to skip the certain failure a farming life would lead to. I would become a success in the world, and money was the path towards that.

In the end it was disappointment that drove us apart. I could not understand how David failed to see the reality of the world and evolve with it. In turn, he was frustrated because I couldn't see the consequences this path would inevitably lead to, and seize the opportunity to shape a better world. In his mind that was the responsibility of our generation.

One night during one of our spring camping trips, David and I sat around the bonfire. Coyotes were howling in the distance. The flames of the fire danced on the surrounding trees with glimmering orange-yellow light. Beyond lay the darkness like a looming abyss.

The others had already returned to their tents and were curled up in their warm sleeping bags. That night around the fire in the safety of that circle of light, David and I shared our plans for the future. We shared how we saw the world and our future roles in it. And as we did, we grew apart even more.

"You mean you're going to be one of those guys in suits?" David asked in disbelief.

"Look around you, David; those men run the world today. What's so bad about business and money? They provide a good living, allow people to have comfortable lifestyles and take care of their families, and they enrich the country."

"You miss the point," he countered. "You forget to question why we need men in suits in the first place. What value do they contribute to society? Yes, I can see they rule the world, but with what right? What entitles them to make a living on the backs of others; make more money than those who contribute real value to the world? They can only do what they do because they are underpaying farmers and all those who feed, clothe and shelter them. They're parasites! Why on earth would you want to become one of them?"

"David, look at how the farmers are struggling," I tried.

"But it's a just struggle!" he blurted.

Going into the business world was a betrayal in David's mind. To him it meant I was abandoning a family, a community and an honorable lifestyle. The only thing he saw was that men in suits shut down farms, foreclosed on mortgages and drove families who had farmed the land for generations to the cities to be employed as cheap laborers in factories owned by the super-class.

To me it was evolution. I was enthralled by the growth of cities, the advancement of science, bigger and faster cars, and ever taller buildings.

A rift was created, a rift so wide that it would only heal with the wisdom of time and the scars that life deals.

Over the summer we traveled together with two other friends to my uncle's cabin in the mountains of British Columbia before we ventured further west. As boys of the prairies, we just had to see the ocean. I remember how we arrived at the coast in White Rock around four in the morning, just before sunrise, the city still at sleep, the ocean at rest, smooth as an untouched liquid mirror waiting for four young men to shatter it with their splashing and send the ripples of their new adventure into the world.

We had fun during that trip. Unencumbered by our futures and political ideas, we drank life and cherished our friendships. I'll never forget the look in David's eyes that morning when we danced on the beach after our swim. In between smiles and laughter, there was this moment of seriousness, a gaze full of love and appreciation for a childhood of camaraderie but with a nostalgic sense and heartfelt pain that it was all over.

Years would pass before I would see David again.

EVA GREEN, DAVID'S MOTHER.

David was smart. He graduated from high school at the top of his class. He excelled in Math and Science, but his heart was in Social Studies. Like all parents we wanted him to go to university; he certainly had the brains for it. But David wouldn't hear of it.

"Mom," he said, "did you know that at some top universities in North America they teach young people like me what they call 'free market economics?' Then they send them to countries of crisis, like to Chile during the time after the assassination of Salvador Allende, to reform the country to a free-market economy. This all happens under the umbrella of the International Monetary Fund, the World Bank or educational assistance. The ultimate goal is to privatize the country's public services and resources. These measures hand control of wealth and power to an elite few while it robs the people of that which belongs to the people: their country and their opportunity for a better life. As a result the people become convenient economic slaves. And because of their dependence, slaves are always ready to serve the masters of the world."

"How do you know all this?" I asked.

"My Social Studies teacher told me," he said.

I cursed the teacher and tried to talk sense into my son. "David, young men go to university to get an education and an opportunity for a better life. You know how difficult it has been to make a living by farming. More and more of our friends have to sell their farms and move to the city in search of jobs. And without an education, you can only find low-paid factory jobs."

"Mom, universities in North America receive significant portions of their funding from corporations and from the upper class, the very people who are waging war on family farms and other small entrepreneurial businesses. I'm not going to allow them to brainwash me to become one of them. I'll study and learn, but will choose my own reading. More importantly, I've decided to take life as my teacher," he said with a self-righteous confidence that bordered on arrogance.

I was concerned he wouldn't seek an education that could help him get ahead in life. But deep inside I was also proud of how steadfastly my son spoke, even though his words were based on hearsay, and at his young age he lacked the experience to give them real power.

"I'm going to travel," he continued. "I'm not sure yet for how long or where my feet will take me. But I want to see the world and get to know it firsthand instead of reading about it in books."

He had saved enough money from his student jobs to last him several months and he planned to work along the way. He was thinking of circling coast to coast through the North American continent. Being born on American soil gave David American citizenship. And given that we as his parents were Canadian, my son carried the passports of both countries. The border didn't exist for David, at least not in the same way as for most of us. Right from birth he always had one foot south of it and the other foot north. In truth, if it was up to him, I don't think borders would exist at all. David was a child of the earth, and borders were something created by man, something that in his mind made no sense at all. He asked me once, "What gives people the right to exclude other human beings on the planet from exploring a part of the world?"

David never ceased to surprise me with the questions he asked. Nothing was beyond examination for him; nothing was accepted on face value. "Are we not all equal and free children on this earth? No one stops a deer when it wanders across the border or the geese when they travel south."

I dreaded the day David planned to leave. When it finally came I hugged him, loving and proud, but also with a fear all mothers feel when their children leave the safety of their home.

"I'll write you," he said.

I still have his letters.

LETTER FROM DAVID TO HIS MOTHER.

Ruston, Louisiana, June 21st, 1978

Dear Mom and Dad,

You've always known that I'm not much of a writer, so I hope you can forgive me for the months without any news and for the time it took me to write this letter. It's not always easy to write you when there is no good news to tell, and I don't want you to worry because I'm doing fine, really, even though my days aren't always easy.

As I told you, I've chosen life as my teacher. I want to experience the good and bad of humanity; learn to understand this world not by reading someone's interpretation in a book, but by witnessing it.

For the last few months I've been traveling through Florida, North Carolina and Alabama, and am now in Louisiana. I've been living with fruit pickers. I figured as a farmer's son, it was best to look for work on a farm. Joining a group of traveling harvesters seemed the ideal opportunity to see something of the country and make some money at the same time.

I did see something of the country and would not trade the experience for anything, but I didn't make a lot of money. Mother, there's a hidden poverty in America you cannot even begin to imagine. And I thought the farmers in Canada were struggling!

Most of the pickers are black; it's like slavery never ceased to exist. But I also met a considerable number of white families who lost their farms and are now serving landowners by picking cotton, tobacco or fruit. As a fruit picker I made four dollars a day! Most of it I gave to the families I've traveled with in return for sharing their shelters and meals.

I've slept in shacks that resemble extended dog houses with no running water, electricity or sewage systems. The walls are decorated with cheap faded prints of Jesus Christ and Martin Luther King. Cornbread and beans are the daily staples. Mothers spice it up differently each time so that at least it tastes like another meal. One time when I was hungry a woman showed me a spot with red clay. That's what they eat when there's nothing else available! They call it, "sweet dirt."

But at night, even when exhausted after at least a twelve-hour day of hard labor, the human spirit still rises. You can hear it in the laughter and the stories that are shared in the light of kerosene lamps while children sleep, sometimes four to a bed. There's no space or privacy, and if it were not for the fatigue it would be impossible to sleep with the constant noise.

They say America is the land where people can realize their dreams through hard work. But I haven't seen any other people working harder than these folks, and I tell you their future isn't going to change any time soon. Most are constantly indebted to the landowners who also own the local supply stores and overcharge the poor laborers.

The saddest thing of all is that these people, who are economically trapped, undereducated and living in extreme poverty, blame themselves because Americans have bought the myth that in this country people will "make it" as long as they work hard enough. This leaves them apathetic and fearful, and so they hardly ever organize or protest—not that I think protesting would help, but a strike might.

I'm not sure if I'll ever be able to enjoy an orange again without feeling the injustice of the slave-like living conditions of these poor souls. It's going to be difficult to ever appreciate the sweet, refreshing juice again. I would gladly eat only half the oranges in my life if it would double these people's income.

But as I said, I wouldn't be writing you if I didn't have at least something good to share.

It's brief, but for a young guy like me, important. The girls are pretty here (smile). I haven't met any yet, or I mean gotten to know any. But I did bump into a pretty young woman this afternoon. She was really cute.

Not sure where my feet will take me over the next few months. This weekend there is a Peach Festival here in town, and I'm sticking around for that. What will come after that, I don't know yet.

I'll write you again in a few months.

With love,

David

As I already mentioned, I set out on this journey to understand my father only after my mother had taken her own life. She didn't speak a word after the events of that fatal day when my father was shot.

To understand my father, you must also see him through my mother's eyes. Her diary offers a window back into time, just like my father's letters. In the end the diary provided me the crucial piece in understanding the events that led to my father's death.

These words were written on those days in the past. I kept the authenticity of my mother's voice, and copied the most important diary excerpts into this tapestry of my father's life.

DIARY OF JODY PALMER, DECEASED, DAVID'S WIFE.

June 25th, 1978.

I have butterflies in my belly. This weekend was the Peach Festival, and I met the most wonderful guy. His name is David and he's from Canada. But he's American too because he was born in this country.

I think fate brought us together. It started with the funniest thing. On Wednesday my girlfriends and I were wandering through Railroad Park.

At one point I was walking backwards so I could see the faces of my friends when I told them that I filed an official complaint with the principal because Mr. Pritchard, our Social Studies teacher, didn't fairly present the abolitionist movement in America. He made it sound like white people were better than black people and that slavery was just a normal course of historic events, not a crime against human rights.

While I was walking like that I could tell from the reactions of my friends that something was up. But I was too passionately enthralled in my story to clue in before bumping into someone. My girlfriends broke out giggling. I turned around and was at a loss for words as I looked into the soft grey eyes of a handsome young man. He was built like Sylvester Stallone, but with a tenderness in his face like John-Boy of The Waltons.

"I'm sorry!" I blurted.

Without a word he smiled at me, and it made me all warm inside. I felt blood rushing to my face and giving it that familiar sunburned color. My friends almost died laughing. It was so embarrassing!

"I'm sorry," I said again, "I didn't mean to . . ."

"Don't worry," he interrupted, saving me from more clumsy apologies. "A pretty girl like you may bump into me any time."

I blushed even more, hid a shy smile and turned around to catch up with my girlfriends. When I glanced over my shoulder I was pleased he was still watching me.

Friday evening I went with my friends to the Peach Festival's concert at Railroad Park. Without telling any of them I searched around, hopeful to see the handsome stranger again. To my disappointment he wasn't there.

On Saturday morning I volunteered in the food booth of our church at the Festival. It was an annual fundraising hit. The booth this year was stacked with homemade baked peach-everything—from tarts to pies, from cookies to muffins. The festival was busy, which was a good thing. The more frantic the booth was, the more I enjoyed it. Time passed more quickly when it was busy.

I could barely keep up with serving people. I handed out a peach pie and returned the change to the customer. When I addressed the next person in line, I saw his friendly face again. Instantly, that warm feeling from our first meeting returned and for a moment I forgot that I was in the middle of a hectic market place.

"You again," he smiled.

"At least there's a table and pie between us this time," I teased.

"Too bad," he said.

"How can I help you? . . . I mean, what kind of pie do you want?" I tried to turn back to the business at hand in the hope of stopping my blushing.

"Peach pie."

I served him. Our hands touched and we had this brief moment, like we had already known each other from a time long gone. Or at least that's how it felt to me.

All good things come in threes, they say. So maybe this is a sign. In the afternoon after hanging out at the arts and crafts fair with my girlfriends, I headed to my favorite event: the peach-eating contest. I lined up to participate, knowing well I couldn't win. I had never been good at stuffing myself with food under the pressure of time. But it was fun, gobbling up as many peaches as possible in a minute. Besides, those peaches were yummy!

Right when it was my turn, guess who stood beside me in the line of contestants? You got it: our handsome young man.

"Seems like we keep bumping into each other," I said and purposely pushed my shoulder against his.

He laughed. "Seems like we do. Maybe it's time we get to know each other. My name is David. It's been nice bumping into you." He laughed again as we lined up for the contest. Then our peaches were put in front of us.

"I'm Jody Palmer," I said and quickly stuffed a peach in my mouth as the contest started. I felt the sweet juice run down my face as, for the first time in a peach-eating contest, I really tried to win— not out of everyone, but I wanted to beat David. Every few seconds we would glance over to see how the other was doing. David's chin was covered with juice as he stuffed the second peach in his mouth while making faces and crossing his eyes to make me laugh. At the forty-five second mark I was howling, tears were rolling down my face, and I couldn't swallow any more peach. David won!

We spent the afternoon chatting about all kinds of stuff. There was so much to talk about. He agreed to meet me in the park for the Peach Jam concert that evening.

I went home to change and couldn't make up my mind on what kind of dress to wear: black and mysterious, white and elegant, or red and provocative. Mom suggested white, Dad said black and I chose red. When we met again, I could see the admiration in his eyes. He liked me . . . a lot.

"You sparkle, princess," he said. Elegantly he offered me his arm and led me without any hesitation to the dance floor. "This demands that I must show you off," he goofed, and made a deep bow before asking my hand for a dance.

David turned out to be a tireless dancer. It didn't matter what kind of music the band would play, his feet were always moving; the dance floor was his home. I had so much fun! Never before had I had a boyfriend who loved to dance just as much as I did. When the band played the latest country slow-dance, "Someone Loves You Honey," I pressed myself against his by now sweaty chest and closed my eyes to savor the moment.

David offered to walk me home. I was glad; I didn't want the evening to end. It was close to midnight. The fifteen minutes it normally took me to cross through the orchards between the town and my home lasted almost an hour.

The night was humid and warm. I love those muggy summer nights with the air that clings around you like a warm, damp cloth. The crickets were singing relentlessly. We walked in silence, enjoying each other's company and the magic of the night. Halfway to my house, David put his arm around me. I laid my head against his shoulder.

When we finally made it to the door of my house, he turned me to face him. Without hesitation, I reached up to kiss him. He answered my desire, and gently our lips touched and our mouths shared our essence. Then we hugged passionately.

Before he left he asked me to go out next weekend.

We're going to a movie. We're going to watch Grease. I heard it's great, with lots of dancing.

This was a perfect day. We played, we talked, we danced, we enjoyed each other in silence and we kissed. I'm in love.

Letter from David to his Mother.

Ruston, Louisiana, November 30th, 1978.

Dear Mom and Dad,

I met a girl. Her name is Jody. She's the daughter of one of the landowners whose peach crop I picked. I met her at the Peach Festival in June. You'll like her. I can't wait to introduce her to you.

Jody has spunk and she genuinely cares for what happens to the people around her. Just like me, she wants to make a difference in the world.

Her dad is quite different though. It's not that he's a bad person; it's just that he has such a different view of the world. He made most of his money on the backs of the poor black people on the plantation, but prides himself on giving a few of them a better-paid job in his chain of grocery stores. He thinks of himself as some sort of do-gooder, but calls these people "niggers" when they're not around.

Jody, on the other hand, truly tries to make life better for the workers even though she doesn't always understand the things that lead to the injustice and poverty she's working to alleviate. Not that I do, but from traveling with the crop pickers I know there is more than meets the eye.

One day, Jody pointed out how the fruit growers are such important financial sponsors of the church programs that try to improve the life circumstances of the poorest. "They not only donate a lot to charity, but the fruit growers also provide jobs for the fruit pickers. What would those people do if these jobs weren't there?" she said, somewhat in defense of the lifestyle of her family.

"But instead of trying to solve the problem through church charities, would it not be simpler for them to raise the wages of the fruit pickers?" I challenged. "Would it not have a more permanent impact and actually reward those people who work the most?"

"But if only one grower does that, his fruit becomes more expensive and he'll lose business," Jody explained.

"You mean his profit will be smaller?"

I could tell from the fire in her eyes that she didn't appreciate my comeback. So instead I tried a different approach, suggesting, "What if the growers of a certain region get together and set a higher minimum wage?"

"And turn this free country into a socialist state!?"

I tried to calm her down; our conversation had almost turned into a fight. "Hey, I'm on your side, remember? We're trying to make a difference. Make things better. And in order to make sure we don't just keep treating symptoms we have to allow ourselves to explore root causes. That's all we're doing here. I'm not accusing you or your family of anything.

"I don't believe anyone gets up in the morning with the thought of making the lives of others miserable. However, reality is, it happens. People do get up and make life worse for other people. I'm only trying to understand why; what's behind it?"

Jody stayed silent for a while. Then she said, "My father always says that social justice is a code word for socialism, and that socialism would destroy this country and rob the freedom for which our ancestors fought."

I must tell you, Mom, some of the perspectives people have here are mind-boggling to me. But it's their reality. The question is, how to help them expand their viewpoint? Jody was one of the more willing candidates to try this with.

"What do you think about social justice?" I invited.

She looked at the sky in thought. She always does that when she ponders something. It's like she expects some divine inspiration from above.

"I believe that the child that's born in a fruit picker's family deserves my help for the simple reason that I can help. I believe that Christ serves as an example of how to live, not only for someone to pray to. Social justice is part of our catechism, and I wouldn't equate our religion to socialism. But I do see my father's point that our government shouldn't force us to care for our fellow human beings, as we are all born free beings. Government has no role in social justice.

It has to come from a person's heart, just like God touches a person's heart through the Church. Government leaves us free in our spiritual path; it should also leave us free to decide how to create a socially just world."

"So you are saying that social justice has no role in politics because it would increase government control through more rules and regulations?" I summarized, and without waiting for the answer I asked, "Does social justice have a role in economics?"

Again she stared into the sky.

Eventually, she said: "I guess it does. Society should be free and equitable, the scriptures say. I don't know enough, though, about economics to decide if the current free market meets those criteria. My father seems to think it's a fair system."

"I'm not an economist either," I said. "But we can see what happens in the world around us. You've talked to the fruit pickers. You've heard their stories of agony; you've seen young adults your age missing a number of teeth because they can't afford the cost of a dentist. You know that right now some families are wandering through America as seasonal laborers because they lost their farms due to a farmer's ill-timed sickness. Do you think those people consider the current economic system to be fair and equitable?"

"When you put it that way it's tough to conclude this system is perfect, it sure doesn't seem to be socially just," she mused.

Even though Jody and I sometimes see things differently, she's just like me. She wants to create a better world and believes it's in our power to do just that.

Together with Jody I'm going to take my adventure, which I started a little over a year ago, to an entirely new level. Jody had been planning to go on a mission trip. We talked about it in the fall and have decided to go on an extended trip together. Her father has given me a job as a shelf-stocker in one of his grocery stores so that I can save up enough money over the winter for the journey. As I said, he actually has a good heart, but he views the world so differently than the way I see it.

"This is the United States of America," he explained one day. "It's the land of freedom and choice, and through hard work the American dream is within everyone's reach. But, not all people make the right choices or are prepared to work hard enough for it.

"I don't know why God doesn't guide poor people to a better life, but He must have His reasons. And it's not up to me to question His plan. The only thing I can do is follow Jesus' example and give to the poor."

But Jesus didn't take from the poor first! Of course I didn't say that; it wouldn't have done any good. He wouldn't have understood my viewpoint anyway.

Based on what I've seen and experienced during my travels, and the conversations I've had, I've come to realize that people form a perspective on the world by looking through an individual lens which each one of us creates as we grow up. I think that when we stop stimulating our own lens, we cease to allow it to expand. When we stop seeking out new experiences, our lens calcifies. When we stop learning and growing, and when we stop considering other people's views, we start judging the world through our limited personal lens. And that is dangerous!

I've come to believe this is a main cause for injustice, anger, violence and even war in the world. I'm not sure though how to deal with this or how to fix it. I only know that I never want to stop challenging myself, I never want to stop discovering. For now though, I'm going to do no different from Jody's father: I'm going to help the people I can help. I'm hoping that over time I'll be able to understand the more systemic issues of our society and make a more significant and lasting impact by addressing those.

In April next year, Jody and I are leaving for one year to work in a mission in El Salvador. The country is currently in turmoil, but please don't worry. We'll be under the protection of the Church.

I'll write you from there.

Love,

David

CARMAN WALSH, 82, RETIRED FRUIT GROWER.

So you're Jody's daughter. How nice to meet you. You look like your mother. You've got the same eyes and that same disarming smile.

Jody's parents' orchard was right next to mine. I remember her being born on that farm. They were good people, the Palmers. Solid neighbors, people you could count on. Never gave anybody any trouble.

I remember when David arrived here in Ruston. That Canadian boy stole one of our southern belles. Jody was one to be seen in those days. A real southern blonde, and with good manners. Who would have thought that God had such a hard life laid out for her?

No one deserves what she went through. Certainly not someone with such a pure heart. First, her parents being killed and then all the tragedy in her own family. That would drive more than one of us crazy.

I heard on the news the horrible thing young David did. Well, I guess he wasn't so young anymore, but that's how I remember him.

He had some crazy ideas way back then. Always hung out with the fruit pickers, even though that wasn't his crowd. But it didn't hurt anyone back then. I guess he and Jody got along so well because she was just like him.

David was always polite to me, to Jody's father, to everyone, really. I never felt that he had anything against us landowners, or for that matter, against anyone else. Sure he was a kid who wanted to create a better world, but don't we all go through that stage as teenagers? A few times when I was visiting the Palmers' house, I would overhear a conversation he and Jody had on such things. It never sounded like he was angry with the world. He just wanted to improve it. I couldn't see anything wrong with that; still can't. Although, I must say, some of his ideas were not thought out very well. He didn't have much understanding of economics. But he had a good heart at that time.

Not sure what brings a man to a point where he loses it and does such a violent thing. But those two sure had to endure their pains in life, and they collected the scars to show for it.

At that time though, they spent just as much time with the church group helping the poor as they spent working. They were determined to make a difference. They even went on an extended mission trip to somewhere in Central America. El Salvador, I believe it was.

Not sure if all this is of any help to you. I can't tell you much more. Only that when I knew David, he had a good heart, beyond any doubt! And anyone who knew him here in Ruston will tell you the same.

DIARY OF JODY PALMER, DAVID'S WIFE.

April 20th, 1979.

Tomorrow David and I are leaving for San Salvador, the capital of the Central American country of El Salvador. Truthfully, I'm terrified. If David hadn't come into my life, I don't think I would have gone through with this mission trip. It was something I always wanted to do, but wouldn't have mustered up the courage on my own. If I had met another guy who wanted me to stay rather than go, it would have been so easy to talk me out of this.

But David, the adventurer, the social justice advocate, the dreamer, the world changer, and most importantly the doer, David only needed to hear a word about the two-week mission trip I had planned in a developing country before he grew the vision into a full-year trip. David doesn't dream small. And once he gets his mind set on something, he'll just do it; nothing will stop him. Terms like, "can't do, impossible, no, stop, dangerous, difficult," and others like that don't exist in his vocabulary. When someone else brings them up, he doesn't even hear them.

I'm so glad I met him. I love him so much! If it weren't for him, I wouldn't be going on this great adventure that lies ahead of us. The mission trip would have remained an admirable aspiration, but something I probably wouldn't have gone through with. It would be safer to stay here, in the world I already know, the world that has shaped my views, the world that has provided me with a good set of tools to operate within it. I'm well-trained to function within the boundaries of this known world.

There would be no need for me to step outside of it and explore the other world out there, there would be no need for me to discover the life of a child that gets born in a crib in that other world, there would be no need for me to learn how a girl grows up to be my age in that other world, nor to understand that girl's view on life or her options for her future; never would I have had any of those needs if it weren't to satisfy my deep inborn curiosity.

"I learned so much when I left home," David said a few days ago, "not only about the world, but also about myself."

"But isn't it scary, isn't it dangerous?" I asked.

"Isn't it boring to stay in your comfort zone?" he questioned in return. "And is life, the great gift we've received, not a waste when we stop growing and exploring; when we stop creating the masterpiece of who we are?"

"I guess you're right, I think as children and young adults we embrace adventure; we all want to travel and explore. I wonder if it's something in our blood, embedded in our genes from the days when we were hunter-gatherer nomads. I think most young people are talked out of such travels by their overprotective parents. But I must admit, if you hadn't come along, it would have been fear that would have held me back."

"Fear is what makes people stop living," David said. "It's the poison that kills the child in each of us. For adults it defines their need for control and security. But control and security are illusions. Every farmer discovers that early on when raising a crop. You never know what curveball God will throw at you. The more attached you are to one particular way of thinking, to one small world in which you've imagined security, the more difficult it will be to handle the curveball. But if you stay flexible, playful, open for whatever ball life might throw at you, you will see every challenge as another opportunity for learning and growth. And exactly because of that lack of fear of losing something, you can only gain. Truth is, you never have anything anyway; we all walk into and out of this world buck naked. But the explorer's attitude increases your chances of hitting the curveball."

David always sounds wise for his age. I think it has to do with his travels. He's been on the road now for more than a year. He's seen a world a lot of my peers haven't. And given his nature, he takes time to think about things, and tries to understand what he discovers.

I'm excited about tomorrow. David thinks that the time we spent with the fruit pickers has been good preparation for the poverty we'll soon be exposed to. I'm so ready to make a difference in this world. It somehow feels like tomorrow will be the start of the rest of my life. I hope it will be a good one.

LETTER FROM DAVID TO HIS MOTHER.

San Salvador, El Salvador, October 29th, 1979.

Dear Mom and Dad,

Where to start? Writing is difficult from this country. There's so much to tell, but if a letter like this falls into the wrong hands it could lead to serious repercussions. I've waited to write you until one of my coworkers in the mission returned to America and could mail it from there.

I'm sure you'll be worried after reading this letter. I've debated a long time whether I should write you at all, but in the end decided you would respect my choice of being here and are probably eager for some news. You have to understand, despite the turmoil and the risks, I want to be here, and so does Jody.

El Salvador is a small and densely populated country in Central America. The standard of living of the small, wealthy elite stands in stark contrast to the quality of life of the poverty-stricken masses. The elite are backed by the military. Death squads, political killings, human rights abuses and disappearances are daily events here. It has made me appreciate the stability and safety of the country where I grew up.

Now don't get too worried; Jody and I are not in immediate danger. We're working for a mission of the Catholic Church in San Salvador. And although the death squads have targeted some churchmen over the last few years, those priests were politically engaged missionaries and often labeled as "communists" by the military government. Earlier this month a military coup established a new junta. The U.S. is providing military support to the new government which should give us more security.

San Salvador, just like the rest of the country, is a city of contrasts. It has close to a million people. About three quarters of them live in the shanty towns that surround the city. The shacks in the squatter communities typically consist of a single room for a family of six to eight people. They are built from tin, cardboard and cloth. There's no electricity, sewers or access to any kind of water. The elite live out their luxurious lives on their estates along the clean streets of the San Benito neighborhood, isolated from this poverty by walls topped with often-electrified barbed wire, and guarded by armed private security forces.

Jody and I teach English in a little Catholic school in the slums and we work with orphaned children in the mission. Don't envision a school like in Canada. We have two small classrooms built of rocks, straw and clay. They have a dirt floor and would compare more to the stalls for our animals at home. The only difference is our rooms have some wooden benches. The children only come to school during the morning. The rest of the day most need to work, or beg on the streets. It's impossible for two working parents to provide for all the basics of the family, so children have to contribute their share of the family income.

Most afternoons, we play games with the orphanage children. It keeps them off the streets and out of trouble. It shows them that some people do care for them.

As you can imagine, we've mastered Spanish well over the past six months.

There is a nine-year-old boy here; his name is Raul. His neighbor brought him to the orphanage together with his two younger sisters. He's such a tenacious boy. He always finds a way to cheer up his sisters and make them laugh despite the burning hell outside these walls. Raul's parents had a little farm just outside of San Salvador. One night, the noise of a truck woke him up. Anonymous gunmen approached his house. His mother put her head through the curtain that separated the parents' sleeping area from that of the children.

"Get out through the window and hide in the bushes!" she ordered in a whisper, with fear in her voice. It was the last time he saw her.

Raul escaped with his two little sisters before the dark-clad men broke through the door. He heard his parents being beaten in the house. He pressed his hands over his ears to block out the screams. Then they took his parents away, never to be seen again. That was two years ago.

The disturbing thing is that this is not an isolated event. This happens every night. The *campesinos*—that's what they call the peasants here—never know if they'll wake up in their bed in the morning, or who in the neighborhood might disappear with the darkness.

One night when I put the children to bed, Raul asked, "Do they steal parents away in your country as well, David?"

"No, they don't," I said.

"Why do they steal them in our country? Why can't we keep our mom and dad just like in your country?"

I didn't know what to answer. Politics don't mean anything to children. Their innocence holds them above matters of power and control; it keeps their hearts pure and allows them to see the essence of things.

"I don't know. But you're safe here," I answered while tucking him in.

"You're a brave boy, Raul, and a good brother to your sisters. I enjoy seeing you play with them. You make them happy. That's important," I said, changing the subject.

"My mom always said that a smile is the seed of love and happiness. She said laughter brings us closer to God. That it can make us feel good, even when it's ugly and dangerous outside; that it's like the light of a candle that pushes back the darkness," the young boy said, recalling the teachings of his stolen mother.

"'In the end, we remember the good things, we remember our love;' that's what she said, and that's how I remember her. I remember her smiling at me and I remember the calm beat of her heart when she held me, curled up, in her arms."

The words of his young wisdom resonated in the silence of the night. His eyes showed love, strength and peace, and I marveled at the resilience of the human soul; its capacity for love in the midst of pain and adversity.

"I like you, David." Raul broke the silence and hugged me. Then he looked at me and said, "I hope they won't steal you away some night."

I held Jody tenderly in my arms that night remembering Raul's words.

"It's always the children who suffer most," I whispered in contemplation. "I'll never allow such greed to harm our children. I promise!"

Yes, it is human greed and the desire for power that's causing all the blood and heartbreak here. When we first arrived in El Salvador, I was shocked. I had seen poverty among the fruit and tobacco pickers in America, but there were no death squads, disappearances and random murders. And while families here live on the brink of starvation, without the most basic needs, the super wealthy are living their lavish lifestyles right next door under the protection of the army and the government. "How can people treat one another like this? ...and what leads to such disparity?" I asked myself. I had to understand what caused the living hell around me.

My search led me to discover the ugliness of the driving powers of our society and the beauty of the human soul that rises above it.

El Salvador's sharp contrast in wealth and poverty today is rooted in colonial times. When the country became an independent republic, wealthy landowners—members of only a few families— formed the national government in such a way that it secured their positions of power and their control over all agricultural land. The landowners turned the nation into a coffee state. Soon they realized the profit opportunity of this crop and expanded their landholdings. Public and communal lands and Indian communities—small subsistence farms that provided for the families of the Indian peasants—were all absorbed into their private estates with the support of the government. The peasants who lost their subsistence farms were turned into cheap plantation labor. The coffee elite formed a strong political oligarchy to protect their land and wealth. Through a political integration with the army generals, the army and national guards' function was to protect the prosperity of the elite. That included quelling any demands from the landless labor force for better working conditions and increased wages, and controlling any unrest and rebellions rooted in the resulting poverty.

Over time the elite diversified their business to include cotton, sugar and cattle as well as insurance, banking, real estate and other corporations. But nothing changed for the landless poor; actually, things got worse. During the last decade large-scale mechanization eliminated a significant number of the plantation jobs, leading to high unemployment. In turn, this has led to more unrest and protest, which has led the army to become even more repressive. To top it all off, death squads, which are believed to be financed by the elite, create fear among the poorest by murdering or kidnapping those who openly challenge or question the government and the unjust economic system.

In the midst of all this, I've also witnessed the best of humanity and the strength of the human soul. That's why we're still here and are planning to stay.

The Church here is a living church, rather than a dogmatic institution that pretends that spirituality is separated from economic and political life, as is often the case in Canada and America. To a large extent this is due to the Archbishop of San Salvador, Monsignor Romero, although it started well before his appointment with passionate priests who decided to set a living example of the life of Jesus. And just like Jesus, several of them paid with their lives. Yes, they were murdered by death squads because the wealthy elite considered them too much of a threat to their way of life.

But despite the threats, Monsignor Romero speaks for the people. He gives a voice to the voiceless poor. He makes the life of Christ come alive in concrete daily situations in the lives of the poor. He preaches a spirituality that sees Christ—the suffering servant— here among the poor *campesinos* of El Salvador. His Sunday homilies are broadcast over the radio and are listened to by the entire nation.

This is what he said and how he sees his role: "I am a shepherd who with his people has begun to learn and understand a beautiful and difficult truth: our faith requires that we immerse ourselves in the world. I believe economic injustice is the root cause of our problems. From it stems all the violence."

Monsignor Romero speaks out whenever human rights are threatened. He has taken on the President, the military and the justice system with regard to the rampant corruption in the country. He has taken on the elite landowners for refusing to give work to desperate and hungry peasants. He has reprimanded the left-wing rebels for their kidnappings and murders. And he has told all of the loyal church-goers from the business and military elite that charity for the poor without justice for the poor has little merit. But he always uses those moments to hold out his hand in forgiveness and ask for a change of heart.

Monsignor Romero is the inspiration, but the people are the true Church (and he would say they are his inspiration). There's a grass roots movement for social justice that has grown from the Church. It's created by activist priests in cooperation with an army of laymen. They call their preachings "liberation theology." The Church here takes an active stance, you see. It calls for an overhaul of the social and political structures—not just a little window dressing by changing some of the rules of the existing structures, but true structural change. And it encourages the congregation to take an active role in bringing about these reforms. The Church trained over fifteen thousand lay preachers who travel the country now. Each of them meets with twenty or thirty local parishioners at each stop to discuss the teachings of God and relate them to what's going on in the country. Together they study the Bible in a way that brings God's words home by relating them to new ways of agriculture, cooperatives, leadership and health. The lay preachers teach the people that before God the poor are equal to the rich.

It's so inspiring to see people rise up in the midst of repression and violence. Peacefully but determined they speak out for justice, love, freedom and compassion. Here at the end of the world, the flame of hope burns strongly. Here at the end of the world, the human spirit demonstrates its resilience, its capacity for love, and its willingness to fight for a better world. Here at the end of the world, spirituality means something. It's alive. Its values, words and prayers are merged into the daily actions of people. The life of Christ is seen as an exemplary life, something to aspire to, not something to contemplate only in Church. Here, people are dying for their cause. Priests are giving their blood for the poor. And every day the crowd grows, despite the rising tension, the increasing disappearances and endless dead bodies.

It's spellbinding. There is nowhere else in the world I would want to be at this moment in time. Not only am I enthralled by what I see happening here, but I've never felt so intensely alive. It's almost as though in the face of danger and death I find all my senses heightened. With magnified vitality I revere the sunshine, treasure a smile and savor a loving touch from a fellow human being.

I think this must be the longest letter I've ever written. It's well after midnight here and I should catch some sleep. Please don't worry; I can feel deep in my soul that I will be fine. But I also know that I have to be here. I'll try to write more frequently to report on the events here.

   With love,

   David

EVA GREEN, DAVID'S MOTHER.

It had been so long since we'd had news. I was overjoyed when the letter arrived in the mail. After reading it I was worried like all mothers worry when their child is in danger. I knew my David. He tried to downplay the risk in order to comfort me. It was obvious that he wasn't safe.

   I couldn't understand. Why wasn't it enough to simply start a farm here at home or go to university? Why did he have to put his life on the line in order to learn what was going on in the world? He could have followed the news like everyone else here; at least that would have kept him safe. And how could one man think he could change the world? Where did he get that drive from?

   But there was also a part of me that was proud. I had raised a good man. A man who cared about his fellow human beings. A man who went out of his way to make a difference. A man who wasn't afraid to face the dangers of the world in order to achieve his dreams.

   My husband wasn't much help. I don't think I've ever seen him troubled about David in his entire life.

"Don't you worry," he said, comforting me in his arms. "He's a man. Men need their adventure. It will pass, and then he'll come home. You'll see, once it gets too hot and dangerous down there, he'll pack his bags and come home. David might be an explorer of life, but he's not stupid."

Despite my husband's sincere attempts to comfort me, night after night I found myself lying awake in bed, imagining the horrors my son could be experiencing at that very moment. In the morning I waited eagerly for the mailman to arrive in the hope he had something for us. When he did, I rushed to the mailbox desperate to find another letter from David.

A postcard arrived with Christmas, sporting the greeting, "Merry Christmas from sunny San Salvador." It was signed, "David, Jody, Raul and all the children." But no report about the events there.

I searched for news from El Salvador in newspapers and caught every mention of it on television and radio. Then months passed without any word from my son, and my fear increased. At times I was beside myself when I imagined my David had disappeared, become one of those anonymous tortured bodies thrown away like trash along the side of a road in a foreign land. All because he wanted to help the children there, all because he wanted to make a difference in this world.

On March twenty-fourth El Salvador was all over the news. Archbishop Romero of San Salvador had been murdered by a death squad, edging El Salvador closer to civil war. My fears increased.

And then the day came. The mailman stopped. I rushed as usual to search the mail for a letter from David. And there it was. My baby was alive!

LETTER FROM DAVID TO HIS MOTHER.

San Salvador, El Salvador, March 31st, 1980.
(mailed from the United States on April 2nd, 1980)

Dear Mom and Dad,

I'm writing this letter from the San Salvador airport. I'm coming home.

The unimaginable has happened. Archbishop Romero was murdered last week on Monday while saying mass in the chapel at the little cancer hospital where he lived. They shot him when he began to offer the bread and wine. Ironically moments before he had contemplated on the Gospel of John: "Truly, truly, I say to you, unless a grain of wheat falls into the earth and dies, it remains alone; but if it dies, it bears much fruit."

Like millions in this country, I was shattered. I felt sick. To make matters worse, as the news was spreading, fireworks were lit in celebration in the neighborhoods of the wealthy Catholic elite.

Last month Monsignor Romero wrote in an open letter to the President of the United States: "You say that you are Christian. If you are really Christian, please stop sending military aid to the military here, because they use it only to kill my people."

And the day before Monsignor Romero was murdered, he called on the enlisted men in the army not to kill their fellow country men: "I would like to make an appeal in a special way to the men of the army, to the police, to those in the barracks," he started. "Brothers, you are part of our own people. You kill your own *campesino* brothers and sisters. And before an order to kill that a man may give, the law of God must prevail that says: Thou shall not kill!

No soldier is obliged to obey an order against the law of God. No one has to fulfill an immoral law. It is time to recover your consciences and to obey your consciences rather than the orders of sin. The Church, defender of the rights of God, of the law of God, of human dignity, the dignity of the person, cannot remain silent before such abomination. We want the government to take seriously that reforms are worth nothing when they come about stained with so much blood. In the name of God, and in the name of this suffering people whose laments rise to heaven each day more tumultuously, I beg you, I ask you, I order you in the name of God: Stop the repression!"

The assassination of Monsignor Romero put the entire country in shock. To top the insult two days after the murder the Americans reconfirmed their commitment to military aid for the government of El Salvador and accused Cuba of having an interest in destabilizing the country.

The day before yesterday, Jody and I joined the tens of thousands for the funeral. People came from all across the country. There might have been close to one hundred thousand people gathered in memory of Monsignor Romero. All together we were mourning our spiritual leader in mass when a bomb exploded and snipers started shooting into the crowd from the rooftops of the buildings that surrounded the plaza. In panic, people fled in all directions. I grabbed Jody's hand and we ran without looking back; there were bullets flying through the air, and people falling, being trampled, bleeding and being killed. If I could have, I would have run straight home.

At that moment I realized this is not my war, even though the following day I reconsidered. Maybe it is? I'm not sure anymore; I'm not sure of anything anymore. Except, perhaps, that this country is going to explode; that I know. Things will get real bad, and it's happening real fast. I just want to take Jody and get out of here.

In the middle of all the confusion, the stress of packing and the making of plans to leave, Raul walked up to me and grabbed my hand.

"Are you leaving me now as well?" he asked with eyes full of desperation.

I so wanted to take him with us, take all those abandoned children with us. But I knew I couldn't. And how could I protect them by staying? What power did I have against the violent forces that were being unleashed? If even the Archbishop couldn't stop or contain them; if even his life was disposable because it was a threat to the lifestyle of the wealthy elite; then what hope was there for these children? I had never felt so powerless in my entire life, and I hated it. It tore my heart apart. It still does.

I had no words for Raul. I knelt down, looked him in the eyes and sent him all my love. I think he felt my struggle, my love and compassion, and my powerlessness. Without a word, I simply held him in a deep embrace. Then turned around and walked away. I told myself I had to focus on the one person I could save: Jody.

I'm not sure though, if I can ever forgive myself for walking away on this innocent boy, on all those children who are not only forgotten by the world, but blatantly trampled on, abused, tortured and killed—all so that the rich and powerful can maintain their luxurious lives! I asked myself what Monsignor Romero would have wanted me to do. I know he would have said, "It's up to you; only you know what God calls you for! Follow your calling and your path."

I also know Romero would have stayed! I tell myself that I'm getting out to save Jody. But the honest truth is: I simply don't have the guts to stay! I'm not ready to die! And those who stand up for the poor and oppressed in this country are being killed. Killed by a government backed by America!

But if I'm not ready to stand up for Raul, what if I ever need someone to stand up for me, for my children, for my family?

I pray for the rebels to win. I pray that in the end love will defeat dollar numbers and egos. And I pray that people might find compassion and respect for their fellow human beings . . . and may God and Raul forgive me for leaving.

Love,

David

EVA GREEN, DAVID'S MOTHER.

I should have listened to my husband. I could have saved myself a lot of nightmares and would have gotten a lot more sleep over the last few months.

A week after receiving David's letter I was in the kitchen putting away the dishes when the door opened.

"Mom, I'm home."

I almost dropped the plates in my hands. My baby was home! My son had returned! The chokehold that had gripped my heart was cut loose in that split second. Overjoyed, with tears streaming down my face, I ran to the front door and took my son in my arms. I felt such relief and realized that children, no matter where they are, always carry a piece of you with them. That day, a piece of me had come home. I was whole again.

When the intensity of our embrace faded, David said, "Mom, I want to introduce you to someone. This is Jody."

"Pleased to meet you, ma'am," greeted a spunky young woman.

That night, I turned a simple meal into a feast. Not only was my family back together, it had grown. My boy had made it safely out of that hellhole and God had been generous and blessed him with love in his life. The way David had written about Jody suggested she was special. And now that I had met her, I knew why.

She was so lively and joyful; it was like she danced through life—drinking it in like it could never hurt; giving herself to it like she could never fail. The better I got to know her over the weeks that followed, the more I realized how lucky David was to have found such a fine woman. Jody walked with the grace of a gazelle, socialized with the cheerfulness of a chipmunk, debated with the focus of an arrow and offered her heart with the softness of an untouched blanket of fresh fallen snow.

That first evening when David had returned we shared stories until late into the night. My husband and I caught him up on things at the farm. Farm life had been steady, though. Nothing had really changed. Just like it had been over the past decade, year after year farming costs had gone up, revenues down, and another set of neighbors had lost their farms to ever larger industrial farming operations.

On the other hand, David and Jody had experienced so much that even weeks after their return they would recount yet another story we hadn't heard. Their stories of peasants in El Salvador and David's time with the fruit pickers in America made me realize how the world had turned into a global village. How the coffee we drank and the oranges we ate were connected to poverty, torture and death in some other place in the world.

"The problem with a global village is that it lacks the moral restraints of a local village," David explained. "See, the growth of the food corporations which are consolidating farmland into ever bigger industrial operations and shipping their products around the world makes the trading of food impersonal. In a local village, you know the people who raise your beef and grow your tomatoes. And if it gets out that a farmer is beating his wife, no one will buy from him anymore. When social pressure is linked to economic security it acts as a moral enforcer in small communities. But in a large impersonal world, there is nothing to keep morals in check other than conscience. And there's abundant evidence that this isn't enough to counter the lure of power and greed."

One night, after David and I had fed all the animals, he sat down in the barn and told me about his departure from San Salvador and about the little boy, Raul. He completely choked up when he recalled his last conversation with Raul and showed me the only picture he had of the little boy. Here was my son, a strong man with the courage of the first explorers, wounded by the world's truths, and his heart torn to pieces by an orphaned nine-year-old boy in a faraway country.

"There was an article about the war in El Salvador in the paper this morning," he said. "It had a picture of a bombed orphanage. It was the one where Jody and I worked. It's where I left Raul. They didn't find any survivors. I had planned to go and search for him when the war ended. But I guess I left him to die."

I could feel the pain of my son's loss. When I wrapped my arms around him in consolation, he sobbed uncontrollably. "I couldn't save him, Mom, I couldn't save him!" he kept repeating while gently stroking the image of the boy. He had managed to keep himself together when fleeing the country, focused on bringing Jody to safety. Now in the safety of his mother's arms he allowed the memory to enter his heart again and the floodgates of emotion to break open.

As a mother I comforted him. As a woman I could feel the desperation of little Raul and how devastating the powerlessness must have felt for my son. And as a friend I had no words of wisdom for David. How do you explain the ugliness in the world? How can you make sense of the pain and injustice? How can you honor truth and make it sound like everything always works out for the better?

Over the weeks and months that followed, David turned inward. He spent a lot of time helping his father on the farm. Whenever we had visitors and the talk turned to El Salvador, poverty or social justice, he left the conversation. When there was news about the country, he changed the television channel. To protect the sanity of his heart, David refused to think about El Salvador and the injustice in the world. He was burying his pain. He was burying Raul.

He was most at peace driving his tractor in solitude over the land. It troubled me, but my husband said, "Don't you worry; the silence of the land is a powerful healer. Just give it some time. The land will take away his pain. His heart will heal."

And like most times the wisdom of the farmer prevailed. During harvest time that year, I noticed David was smiling again. He teased Jody more often and they laughed and played together. A wise, understanding woman, Jody had waited with patience, giving David time to work through his pain, being there for him when he needed a caring embrace. Now, love was touching his soul again and joy had returned to his heart.

As we went into winter and the land lay dormant, David spent all his energy and attention on making Jody happy. I was hoping that soon he would make his love for her official.

DIARY OF JODY PALMER, DAVID'S WIFE.

March 20th, 1981.

David proposed to me today. I've been waiting for this moment since the day we met. I knew when I first saw him almost two years ago that I wanted to marry him. Like with everything David does, his proposal was unique. It had a magical simplicity and a tender sincerity that burned the memory deep into my soul.

The weather this morning, on this first day of spring, was pretty grey. The temperature rose just above freezing, and it rained— pretty normal for the season in this part of the world. Once in a while the drizzle turned into wet snow, but none of the white stuff would accumulate on the ground anymore. By late afternoon the clouds started to break up and the sun managed to throw some of its warming rays onto the drenched land.

"Hop in the truck, I need to show you something," David said. "Make sure to dress warmly and put on some hiking boots."

"Where are we going?"

"You'll see!"

The way he said it I knew that probing more was only going to lead to agitation without answers. I had learned to go along with his requests when he was acting mysteriously. And why would I not? The man loved me dearly, and when he was behaving like this it was always a prelude to a surprise, thoughtfully put together to make me laugh or feel loved.

Soon after we were on our way, I guessed where we were going. He was heading towards the Cypress Hills, the highest location in the province and David's favorite place in the region.

During the summer he would take off and spend days hiking in the forests and the hills. At times I joined him, but he enjoyed his solo trips as well. He claimed I was too noisy to see any of the wildlife. The past summer we often went swimming in Elkwater Lake. The area was so different from the open plains where the farm was. The hills were carved with mountain streams and flanked by lush evergreen forests that sheltered an abundance of animals.

Ever since he was twelve David had been hunting with his father in those hills. As a result he knew the terrain and wildlife trails as well as the creatures that call the place home.

By dusk we stopped in Battle Creek Valley at a trail leading to the Conglomerate Cliffs. You could drive straight up to the top of the cliffs, but David almost always chose to hike there. "You've got to connect with the land in order to appreciate the vista the cliffs reveal," he would say. The temperature had fallen well below freezing. Snow still covered the forest floor here and reflected the bright light of the full moon, dressing the landscape in a crisp silver glow.

Without a word we started hiking to the top of the cliff. The forest was alive in the silence of the night. Coyotes howled, an owl called, and deer bolted, soundless like dark shadows, into the blackness of the forest when we approached. On any other day it might have scared me, but tonight with the light of the moon and guided by my loving man, I felt at peace, so I allowed the magic of the night to touch my soul.

When we reached the crest of the cliff I was treated to a mystical panorama. Below us was Adams Lake, still covered with ice and a blanket of snow. Behind it, soft glowing hills melted in the distance into the flatness of the prairies, home to farmers' fields. A breathtaking halo had formed around the full moon. David stepped behind me and wrapped his arms around me. In silence we took it all in.

"You know why these hills are higher than all the surrounding land?" he asked. "These hills, and especially these Conglomerate Cliffs, are protected by an armor-like cap-rock that prevents any wind and water erosion. That cap is like my love for you. It will always protect you so that your spirit can shine like a jewel in a world that weathers the hardships of time."

I turned towards him. I wanted to see his eyes as he spoke. For a moment he hesitated, not because he was afraid, but because his emotions almost got the better of him.

"Today is the spring equinox, a time of harmony, of balance between the male and female forces of our universe. The full moon shines above us tonight. That means it is a good time to seed.

"You know I'm a man of little means. I'm a simple farmer and can only offer a simple life."

He knelt and took my hand. I gasped, knowing what would follow.

"Jody, I love you with all my heart. I have no diamonds to offer you, except my heart. Will you marry me?"

With tears in my eyes I wrapped my arms around him and passionately kissed him. "Yes, I will," I whispered in harmony with the voices of the forest.

"Then take this as a sign of my love for you. I carved it from a piece of the protective capstone that preserved these hills through time."

He handed me a grayish-green circular rock with a hole through the center. A leather string looped through it so that I could wear it as a necklace.

I pressed it against my heart. This polished charm carried David's love, creativity and protective cover.

"I'll always wear it," I said.

I cuddled in his arms and we stayed on the edge of the cliff grateful for each other, grateful for our love, grateful for this night and the extraordinary setting that surrounded us. We were so small, so insignificant in this world, yet our love was as powerful as the magic of this night. Hand in hand we walked back to the truck.

We didn't return to his parents' farm. David had arranged another surprise: an overnight stay in a close-by log cabin that belonged to one of his friends. During the drive we sang along with REO Speedwagon's latest song, "Keep on Loving You." That night, between the blankets in the romantic cabin, we sealed our engagement with passionate lovemaking.

David is sound asleep now. But I can't sleep. I don't want this magical day to end. I decided to write down the events so that when the details of the past have faded, we will still be able to cherish them.

I'm in love! I'm getting married! I'm the happiest girl in the world!

EVA GREEN, DAVID'S MOTHER.

Sometime in the spring of eighty-one, David announced he and Jody were getting married. I was of course very happy for them. But they were still so young! I must admit that this concerned me a bit. Most of his friends were still at university. Starting a family and making a commitment to someone for life was a big responsibility. When we had a moment alone and I asked him if he really wanted to do this, wanted to commit to Jody for life, I saw that same fire in his eyes like years ago when he had taken his little bike and ridden to his father in the city. He didn't run away this time, but I was wise enough to drop the subject and reassure him that his father and I were supporting him.

"She's a real nice girl, that Jody. We love her and I know you'll make each other happy. If the two of you think this is the time to get married, then we better start planning the wedding!"

They got married in the fall of that year. They had found a more progressive priest in Saskatoon to marry them; he had done mission work as well. When I asked why none of the local priests were good enough, David explained, "Mom, we searched hard to find the right priest. First, I want to marry in paradise, in God's first Church."

"And where might that be?"

"In nature, God's creation, not man's," he said. "And second, it's important to me that our marriage is blessed by a spiritual leader who understands what a living church is and can reflect that in the ceremony. Most priests here don't get the concept."

The marriage ceremony took place on top of the Conglomerate Cliffs. The vista of the foothills was colored with the vibrant shades of fall: yellow, orange and red underlined by satin-glowing evergreen forests closer to the cliffs.

The place was truly paradise. No creation of man would ever match the magnificence of the scene around us. The ceremony was graceful in its simplicity, from Jody's elegant but modest white dress to the fallen logs that served as seats.

It was a small wedding. When, together with Jody's parents, we had made a list of all the family and friends we wanted to invite, Jody and David had trimmed it down to close family and a dozen friends.

"We want a private and intimate wedding, not a grand one," David had explained.

Together with the Palmers we wanted to give the couple tickets to an exotic destination for their honeymoon, but they didn't want to hear about it. So instead they took off for two weeks to the Big Horn Mountains in Wyoming. They both fell in love with the area, so when years later they bought a small farm in the proximity of those mountains it didn't really surprise me.

Although at first I had been concerned about their young age, I soon realized this had been the best thing that could ever have happened to David. As a married man, he focused on taking care of his wife. He had buried his war with the world. There was no talk about making a difference anymore. It looked like he had surrendered to the ways of the world and was going to live according to its rules. He had decided to love and find happiness within the boundaries the world had set for him. So, he threw himself completely into the agribusiness and was determined to develop a thriving farm, one that would grow and keep up with the times so that it could provide for his family. My husband and I decided we'd help them. So we split off a parcel of our land that still had the old farmhouse of my husband's parents on it and allocated that section of the farm to our son's business.

Finally, David had someone and something to live for, something that was tangible. A purpose, a way for him to make a difference that was within his reach. He had seen enough of the world to appreciate how good we have it here in Canada, and finally had accepted that as a blessing rather than as a curse.

Soon after the two lovebirds had come back from their honeymoon they shared with us that they were going to welcome children as soon as they were blessed with them. I started looking forward to becoming a grandmother.

DIARY OF JODY PALMER, DAVID'S WIFE.

May 1st, 1983.

I'm pregnant! Today, I found out that I'm pregnant. I had been late now for several weeks with my period. Given my irregular cycles a week late is not unusual, but this time I was long overdue. I didn't feel nauseated in the morning or show any other sign of illnesses which women often complain about in their first weeks of pregnancy. But I had noticed my unusual appetite for pickles. David's mouth fell open last week when I put pickles on my burger. I shrugged my shoulders. "Tastes can change, you know," I said. I must admit it did surprise me as well.

Now I understand.

When we decided to allow children to enter our lives a little over a year ago, I burned (I guess I should write "peed") through a pregnancy test each month as soon as I thought I was a day late.

According to David's mom and several of her friends from the bridge club, my irregular cycle was a challenge for getting pregnant. But David and I were in no rush. We had agreed that we would let life take its course and let any pregnancy be a surprise. So after wasting pregnancy tests for four months, I stopped peeing on the little strips that weren't giving me the right color anyway. This morning I had the feeling I was seriously overdue. So when David was on his tractor harrowing the field, I drove to the pharmacy to buy a pregnancy test.

As soon as I had paid, my curiosity got the best of me. I couldn't wait any longer. So I paid a visit to the store's bathroom. I had to know right then. I peed on the little strip and then sat there on the toilet seat staring at the strip, waiting for it to show me two purple colored bands. According to the instructions it was supposed to happen within three to five minutes. Waiting on the toilet seat, I realized how long a minute really was.

After about two minutes someone knocked on the door. I ignored them; I was busy. They had to wait or go somewhere else since I wasn't moving until either this strip showed me some colors or five minutes passed. I was so anxious that I couldn't keep my toes still! If I had been a nail biter, I would have had none left. I kept a close eye on my watch. Three minutes and sixteen seconds and there it was: two purple color bands. At first I was in shock and disbelief. It had really happened! Then I felt a deep gratitude; there was life growing inside of me, a child, the fruit of love, our love, the love between David and me. I felt really special; I could do this! I was pregnant!

I jumped up from the toilet and felt like yelling and screaming with excitement. But then I remembered the person waiting outside, so I did a quiet little jiffy dance before collecting myself again and walking out with a smile that reached from ear to ear across my face.

When I got home, I ran through the field towards David. He stopped the tractor and at first thought something was wrong.

"I've got something to tell you," I said, the same smile still on my face. "But I will only tell you on top of the Conglomerate Cliffs." I had decided to save the announcement and make it in what had become a special location for us. I grabbed his hand and pulled him into a run because I had no idea how long I would be able to keep this news to myself. On the drive over I fiddled nervously with my hair. David kept glancing at me with curiosity in his eyes. The by now engraved smile on my face betrayed that whatever I had to tell wasn't just good news, but great news. "Skip the hike; let's drive straight to the cliffs," I directed, eager to share the news.

"What's gotten into you?" he yelled over the wind as we got out of the car. My excitement made him laugh, and giggling, we both ran to the edge of the cliffs. There I faced him and pulled him close to me. Then I took his hand and placed it on my belly. Before I said anything, he knew; I could see it in his face.

"I'm pregnant," I said. "Our child is growing inside of me. Say hello to your baby."

His eyes sparkled with happiness and he lovingly embraced me. "I'm going to be a father," he said in disbelief.

He knelt down and kissed my belly.

Before heading back we strolled hand in hand along the trail that snaked along the top of the cliffs, enjoying the magnificence of creation. I realized there were now three of us. We were a family!

LETTER FROM DAVID TO HIS SON.

Maple Creek, Wednesday, December 21st, 1983.

Dear Tom,

Welcome to this world. It's been a long harrowing ride to arrive here. Over the last twenty-four hours I feared for both your life and that of your mother. I've been through emotional highs and lows, the devastating fear of losing my loved ones and then the joyful ecstasy of regaining you both. Words fall short to express how I feel. I love you, I love your mother, I love you both so much, and I'm so glad the last two days came to a happy ending. My precious little family is safe now.

It's one in the morning. I've been up now for some forty-two hours with hardly any sleep. The adrenaline is still flowing through my veins. I just returned home and still can't sleep. The house is quiet and empty. It seems our home already misses you and your mom. I miss you both. I've taken these pages to write your birth adventure now while the emotions are still raw and the memory fresh. I'll save this letter for your eighteenth birthday so you'll know how you entered this world and how much you are a child of love.

On late Monday morning your mom was ironing some clothes when she called me and said, "David, it's started."

I was fixing up an old meat-slicer. I was so focused on my work that I didn't immediately clue in.

"What's started, honey?" I asked without looking up.

"We're going to have a baby!" she said, excited but with an air of serenity.

"What? Oh, honey, that's great!"

I flew up from my task. Jody had her hands on her humongous belly and was smiling softly. A few minutes later a painful grimace wiped her smile away and her eyes betrayed her anxiety. She had been warned about the painful road that lay ahead—a mother's burden to bring new life into this world. She realized there was no turning back now; the time to face that pain had come.

"What should I do? Is there anything you want me to do?" I asked.

A few seconds later her face cleared up again and she comforted me, "No, it's not bad yet. The contractions are still far apart. I'll start timing them. The doctor said to come to the hospital when they are at about five minute intervals."

Jody spent most of the afternoon on the couch reading and watching some television. I made sure to take good care of my princess and served her anything she wished for.

When by late evening the contractions were still only every nine minutes, we decided to go to bed. Neither of us slept much that night. Your mother's groans of pain intensified and the pauses between them slowly decreased. I felt guilty laying next to her without sharing some of that pain or being able to make things better for her.

But I was also excited at becoming a father. I imagined how you and I would play together. We knew you were a boy. We had asked the doctor to tell us since neither of us could stand the suspense of not knowing. We didn't tell anyone your name yet, even though shortly after we knew you were a boy, and after some lighthearted bickering between the two of us, we decided you would be called Tom. Your name was inspired by a book we both read during the time I first knew your mom. It made a deep impact on both of us.

It's called *Uncle Tom's Cabin*. You should read it sometime when you're old enough. Tom is a name for a righteous and brave man.

The nice thing about naming you before you were born was that over the past months we talked to you, calling you by your name. We played with you by pushing Mommy's tummy. We always enjoyed how in response you pushed back with your feet. When your mother was doing something that wasn't comfortable for you, you sure let her know by kicking those feet real hard.

Just when I had drifted off to sleep in the early morning, Jody woke me up again.

"David, it's time to go to the hospital. The contractions are a little more than five minutes apart."

I don't think I'd ever woken up that fast. I jumped out of bed and into my clothes. It was early in the morning and still dark. Like a madman I ran outside to get the truck started, to warm it up. Once in the truck, I cursed myself for forgetting the keys so I had to run back inside (I normally never forget such things).

When the truck was finally warming up, I assisted your mother in getting dressed. I draped a warm coat over her before helping her through the freezing cold to the truck. The air bit straight through any spot of exposed skin. You picked a bitterly cold winter day to come into this world, my son.

Jody moaned again in agony. So I sped out of the driveway and almost slid into the ditch when I turned onto the country road.

"Did you grab the bag with my things?" Jody asked.

We had it all prepared weeks ago, and the bag with toiletries, sleeping-gown, slippers, books and some other stuff was standing right by the door—still. I thought I'd made sure we could zip out of the house and be on our way to the hospital in no time! In fact, I had run the scenario through my head at least a hundred times. Now it seemed like I had lost my mind; luckily your mother was still thinking straight.

We returned to the house to pick up the bag. Before driving off again, Jody put her hand on mine and said, "Honey, I'm having a baby, I'm not dying. Just get me to the hospital and not in a ditch!"

Then she had another contraction. As she moaned my foot gained weight and sped the truck towards the hospital.

The drive seemed to last forever. I estimated that due to the slippery conditions of the road the normally half-hour drive would take at least ten extra minutes. About halfway to the hospital, Jody turned up her groaning volume. I knew her pain had intensified, and so again my foot became heavier. The front of the truck caught a snow drift and once more we flirted with the ditch. I slowed down, then heard the aching woman beside me doing breathing exercises in between contractions, and faster we went again.

Upon arrival at the hospital, I rushed to the other side of the truck to help my laboring wife get out of the truck. But I slid on the ice and ended up flat on my back beside the vehicle. Jody opened the door and in between her bursts of pain, a ridiculing smile graced her face as I crawled back up onto my feet. What had happened to my calm collected self?

The hospital allowed me to relax a little; at least now my beloved wife was in capable hands. "Now, it will all be over quickly," I thought.

I couldn't have been more wrong.

When the nurses checked your mom, the bad news came. After almost eighteen hours of labor, my lovely wife had barely any dilation and her pain was rising. The nurses decided to wait it out for another few hours.

At sunrise the doctor came by for a visit. Jody's dilation had progressed a little. He suggested she hang in there, and promised to return sometime after lunch.

Meanwhile your mother's pain kept intensifying and she was burning out. Her soft groans had been replaced by subdued yelps. She entered a trance-like state in an attempt to hold on. She needed every ounce of energy to stay collected and focused. I was beside myself from seeing my wife suffer without being able to do anything for her. As a result I became increasingly frustrated with the nurses. "At least there should be someone who can do something," I cursed.

When the doctor returned, your mother was still only half-dilated. He decided to break her water to speed up the process. I thought I had seen your mother suffer already—but as soon as the doctor broke her water, it was like all hell broke loose. Jody's controlled yelps transformed into wild screams. The burning contractions came now every couple of minutes, and when they did, her body had the uncontrollable urge to push. She wasn't allowed to give into it though, due to the marginal dilation.

But the pain had taken over, and your mother had lost control of her actions. The nurses were on her case for being unable to control the pushing convulsions of her body and for the unrestrained screams. But my wife didn't care anymore. She was in a different space, unaware of anything around her. Her world had been reduced to a relentless unbearable agony. She screamed her head off, and during the short pauses tried to regain her strength to confront the next wave of pain which was inevitably on its way.

By now I was frantic, angry at everything and everyone for not being able to help my wife. Then in between two contractions, Jody grabbed my arm and with desperate but commanding eyes whispered in exhaustion: "Help me! Make them help me! Make the pain stop. I can't keep this up. Help me, David!"

That was it! I was done being a spectator. My wife needed me. After I had a blunt conversation with one of the nurses, the doctor came by again and this time offered alternative solutions. Jody opted for a Caesarean section with an epidural anesthetic. If you weren't going to be born the natural way, your mother wanted at least to be conscious when you came into this world.

By four o'clock that afternoon, after twenty-seven hours of suffering, your mother was relieved of her painful ordeal by the epidural. It was somewhat odd. Within minutes she was smiling again, still exhausted but visibly relieved that the contractions weren't hurting anymore.

At around six p.m. I kissed your mother goodbye as she was rolled to the operating room. About an hour later, a nurse came for me. She handed me a green sterile gown, cap and face mask. Once dressed like a surgeon I was rushed to the operating room; the doctor had given me permission to be with your mother during birth.

Your mom smiled when she saw me come in. It was a smile that radiated her love for me, relief that it was almost all over, and joy of anticipation to finally meet you.

I stood beside her and held her hand. The nurses gave me a chair.

"Don't pass out on us," they warned. "We can't take care of more than one patient in this room! Don't be ashamed to sit down, either; most husbands can't handle seeing this."

Then the doctor took his scalpel and sliced through your mother's stretched skin. I kept glancing over the screen they had placed on top of your mother's belly so she couldn't see the procedure. When the doctor had access to the womb, he used two big clamps to stretch the skin open before reaching in with his hand.

I asked Jody how she felt.

"I'm fine," she said. "It's kind of weird. I feel all the pulling but nothing hurts."

The next moment, the doctor pulled his hand back out and with it came your head. With big dark eyes you stared straight at me, your body still in the comfort of your mother's womb, your eyes curiously taking in the world which you were about to enter. I'll never forget that moment, the way you looked into my eyes and the realization that you were part of me, born out of the love between your mother and me. You were a part of us—a vulnerable part to protect; an innocent part to love; an independent part to eventually let go of; and a younger part that, in the end, will live on when we're gone.

The doctor slid both his hands into your mother's pried-open belly and grabbed your shoulders. The moment of entry was then; he lifted you from your mother's womb. You weren't crying as I had seen most newborns do in movies. The doctor put you in your mother's arms before he clamped off and cut the umbilical cord. Tears of love and happiness rolled down your mom's face.

Then you coughed. It sounded full of mucous. The nurses went into action, took you from your mother, and before I realized what was happening, tubes were being put up your nose.

"He's having breathing problems," one nurse explained while frantically continuing to rehabilitate you. You got worse, and I felt my heart being taken into a chokehold. You had barely been in our lives and already I loved you so much! It was much too soon to face the real possibility of losing you.

Another nurse came to assist in your rescue; the doctor had his hands full with your mother.

Eventually a needle and an oxygen mask did the job, and finally you screamed your lungs out. "Don't worry, that's a good sign," the nurses reassured me, seeing the concern on my face. Then they measured and weighed you in a different room. I stayed with you, and when they were all done they escorted both of us from the operating area to your mother's room where we had to wait until she was sutured up.

Then the moment came when the nurses put you into my arms. I was clumsy holding you, and they had to demonstrate how to give proper support to your neck. Then we sat together on a chair, waiting.

I couldn't keep my eyes off you. I was in awe of the miracle of creation. Here you were, our little baby, with five little perfectly-formed fingers on each hand, and the same with the toes on each of your feet. Your breathing was rhythmic and calm now; you were peacefully sleeping in my arms. Your skull had a large cone shape to it, but the nurses had told me not to worry about it. It had been due to the pressure Jody had put on your head during labor, and I imagined the headache that must have caused for you. The nurses assured me that in a few days your head would look totally normal. Meanwhile, I had draped the white shawl in which you were wrapped over the back of your head to conceal the big bump there.

An hour passed, and your mother still hadn't returned. It had been a long day with lots of unexpected turns. I was tired. I told myself Jody was in good hands and forced myself to focus on the image of taking you both home; on seeing you sleep in the nice baby room we had prepared for you; on imagining your mother feeding you. Another hour went by. No Jody yet, nor any news from any of the nurses. This was taking too long.

My imagination took a turn. What if something had gone wrong with the surgery? What if something had happened to your mother? I looked at you and realized the responsibility I had. Was I ready to raise you on my own? How would I feel about you if your birth had caused Jody to die? As my mind took me through the dark corners of my soul, minutes turned into hours. My entire world collapsed again.

I heard some noise down the hallway and listened intently. Steps approached our room. The door swung open and two nurses rolled your mother into the room. Relief flooded my soul. Your mom smiled and the first thing she did was ask for you. She cradled you in her arms. And despite her exhaustion, she glowed with happiness and reverence.

You had your first taste of the milk of her breasts. Then I lay next to your mom and the three of us fell peacefully asleep. Shortly before midnight I woke up and started for home.

The silver light of the full moon lit up the night, for it was reflected on the snow-covered landscape. The world seemed so much more vibrant tonight. In the silence of solitude with the rumbling of the truck's engine in the background, I dropped my guard and allowed the events of the day to touch my heart. And as they did, tears rolled down my face. Tears of happiness; tears for having been saved a most terrible loss; tears in awe of the miracles of creation; tears of gratefulness for the blessings in my life. Tonight is the longest night of the year, tomorrow the light returns to the world—a light that will be more colorful due to your presence in this world.

Use your life well. Be grateful for it, and as I once read: Live each day like it could be your last; dance through life like no one is watching; and love without the fear of ever being hurt.

Welcome to this life, my son. Your mom and I love you beyond words and will always be here for you!

With love,

Your father

When my grandmother gave me the testimonial that follows, she did address it to me and said things like, " ...when you were born." But to avoid any confusion for you, the reader, in trying to understand my father, I have taken the liberty to adjust this testimonial as well as most other ones where people talked about my childhood and have inserted my name whenever my grandmother or others referred to me.

EVA GREEN, DAVID'S MOTHER.

The years that followed Tom's birth were the happiest of times for David and Jody. I'd like to think they were blessed with so much joy during that period that it gave them the strength to bear what was to come.

Even though Jody's first childbirth experience had been unusually severe, mothering baby Tom made her forget all about it, and soon she was pregnant again. Just over two years after Tom's birth, Tessa was born and this time without any complications. They now had a boy and a girl, and truly were the perfect farming family. David worked hard not only to keep the farm, but to expand it.

"It's the only way, Mom," he explained. "Either I go with the times, keep up with the latest technology, and grow, or I'll lose the farm like all those other families over the last decade."

Jody was a great mother and devoted all her time and energy to the children. Her only distraction was her vegetable garden. "I want my children to eat healthy," she said to David. "You know I don't want any of that chemical stuff you pour onto the fields on our vegetables. I know they say it does no harm to anyone, but I don't want to be eating it."

On Saturday evenings David and Jody had "date night" and the little ones would come and stay with us. I always looked forward to Saturdays. Sometimes the grandchildren came for an entire day or weekend while my son took his wife out for a hike in the hills or a short weekend trip.

The children had their own room in our house. They got along so well. Not only was it a pleasure to play with them, but I could watch them for hours.

At the age of four little Tom would drag his sister with him everywhere he went. He would stand her up against him, bend through his knees, slap his arms around her waist, lift her off the ground and lean backwards to balance the weight. Then he would wobble around to where he wanted to go and put her back down. If he got tired of carrying her, he would simply drag her across the floor by her arm. When he did, she would giggle her head off. Tessa didn't get much time to play with dolls, even though she had amassed a collection from Santa and birthdays. Tom would put tractors and cars in her hand and tell her what to do. He was the play director and

Tessa a very willing playmate.   But although Tom took the lead, he was never selfish. He always looked after his little sister.

I had a cookie jar, like all grannies do, and the children knew very quickly what the rules were to get the jar to open. At supper they had to empty their plates in order to get a cookie. Tom was a good eater. You could put anything in front of him and he would gobble it up. But Tessa was a different story. If it wasn't mashed potatoes or applesauce, chances were good she didn't like it, and if there were any other vegetables other than tomatoes, she would stubbornly leave them on her plate. But she loved cookies. And so when supper was over and I started to clean up and bring things back to the kitchen, Tom would quickly empty Tessa's plate.

"Tessa's done," he would say when I returned, with his mouth still full of her food. "Can we get our cookies now, Nanny?"

Tom always made sure his sister wouldn't be short of anything.

Every Sunday the entire family would visit the local community church. It had become a family tradition that after church the family would come and visit. I always made sure I cooked a special meal.

At Christmas David and Jody would take the children for two weeks to visit Jody's parents in Louisiana. At least that was until the year they died in that horrible car accident, God rest their souls.

Since Christmas was in Louisiana, Thanksgiving was at our home. The children always came and stayed with us for two days. David and Jody would go hunting in the hills the day prior, and return the morning of Thanksgiving to celebrate family and harvest.

We always played games with the children. They loved to play card games. But David would get mad at me if I let them win or

cheated to that end. Especially when I would secretly change cards
with Tom to let him triumph over his father.

"Mother, they need to learn to play fair and know that losing
isn't the end of the world," David would say. But fathers don't
understand that grandma's function is to support their grandchildren,
no matter what. And if it meant cheating to make them happy, that's
what I did.

Tom and Tessa were so adorable. Children can say such
sincere innocent things. After one of those Thanksgiving dinners both
kids were snuggled against me while I sat on the couch. I think Jody
felt kind of bad for me with the weight of two children on my lap, so
she suggested that one of them sit with her.

"No, Mommy," Tom said. "When we're home we sit with
you. But at Nanny's we sit with her. She's softer. You know it's like
bananas; the older they get, the softer they become."

Jody and I chuckled as Tom paused in thought, took my hand
and checked my skin. Then he turned to me and asked with concern
in his voice, "When you get even older, Nanny, will your skin also
turn brown?"

I so enjoyed those years. The pictures are still decorating
my walls. They help me remember the good times.

David had a loving wife and a perfect family. I know his
world-changing ambitions were only sleeping beneath the surface, and
I always wondered if they would have stayed dormant—if he would
have taken satisfaction in being a farmer and a father—if he hadn't had
to endure the pain that was to come. For even though he didn't
discuss any of his idealistic views anymore, I knew his deep sense of
justice hadn't changed, and that at times he was conflicted about his
own actions.

David had a particularly hard time when his neighbor went broke and had to sell the farm. David ended up buying the man's machinery and land at the public auction where the estate was being sold. And he got it at a real bargain.

"Mother," he said, "what was I supposed to do? Someone was going to buy it anyway. If I hadn't made my bid, they would have gotten even less. I know I've profited from their demise and it doesn't sit well with me. But I don't know what else I could have done. It's dog eat dog, and I hate it. But that's the way the system is set up. And until the day it changes, I have to play by its rules if I want to take care of my family."

And so the farm expanded, the equipment grew larger, the debt increased and the distance between the farmer and the land grew wider while the conflict in David's soul ripened in silence.

RAY BERENDORF, 69, RANCHER.

I knew David from the time he was a kid, mostly through his father. David's father was a good man. I didn't see David all that much. I ran into him only at farmers' markets, the hardware store, the rodeo or the fair; the typical places where we all had some business.

We farmers are loners, you know. We're more comfortable with the land and our animals than with people. People are too complicated. They make a mess of almost everything, and in particular, those crooks who run this country these days. Seems the dumbest chickens have taken control of the highest spot in the roost.

I didn't care much for David. I know you're his daughter and all, but you asked me to talk straight with you.

I thought David was trouble from the time he was a teenager and he grew his hair long. That told the whole story right there. And instead of helping his father when he came out of high school, he went on the dole for a few years. The young people these days don't have the same manners or responsibility that my generation was raised with. They take everything for granted, and don't take care of things anymore, including themselves.

I was raised in a time when you respected what you had because you had to earn it. We were grateful for things. We groomed ourselves properly, took care of our family, including our parents, respected the land, and worked hard. There was satisfaction in good labor. These kids today treat work like it's a curse. If something needs to be done and they can't find a big enough tractor or some other piece of machinery to do the job, they're all lost.

Just the other day, I passed by two young fellows who were trying to pull a guy's car out of the ditch on a snow-covered road. The snow was hard-frozen, like early morning snow can be after a day of warm weather. The white stuff was up to the car's windows; that's how deep it was stuck in there. And the guys were just sitting in their truck spinning their tires on the ice-covered road without moving that chained-up car an inch. I stopped to help; that's what we do here when someone is stuck or has a problem.

"We can't get her moving," one of them said. "Maybe if we chain your truck to it too we might get her out."

I looked the scene over and just shook my head. There was no way that car was going to move without shoveling.

"Don't you think we should clear the snow away first?" I said.

"With what?" the reply came.

"What's wrong with a shovel?" I asked.

"That's a lot of snow to dig," one of them grumbled.

"Well, we better start at it or we'll still be here tomorrow," I said, grabbing my shovel out of the truck. I began digging. Reluctantly they took up their own shovels and joined me. Half an hour later we'd cleared all the snow around the car and pulled it out without really even trying. I still wonder how long they would have tried pulling that vehicle if no one would have had the common sense to roll up their sleeves, commit to some work and get the job done.

I must admit, when David returned from his travels, he did help his parents. And he brought a girl home with him; she was a friendly gal. I guess that was one good thing that came out of it. According to his father, David had been somewhere in Central America and had seen some bad stuff. There had been some kind of war down there, and he'd seen some of it. I tried to get David to speak about it one time, but he only said, "I don't talk about that time anymore," and that was the end of it. A man knows when to stop being nosy. So I left it at that.

I never figured David out. As a teenager he walked and talked like a hippie. Nothing in this world was good enough, and it all had to change. Then he came back from his travels, started his own family and completely trampled the traditional ways of farming by embracing those factory-farming methods that were destroying our communities—the very things he was concerned about as a teenager! He just went from one extreme to the other.

Why was it so difficult to simply respect the way things were and keep them like that? Sure we had to work hard when I was his age, but the land kept producing for us. We had control over our market, and the quality of our produce was a hundred times better than the crap they put into stores today.

Most people haven't experienced the rich flavors of carrots, tomatoes or beans. These days, it all tastes bland. Nothing is grown anymore for its taste, but rather for how long it can be preserved so that it can travel further.

When David's parents set him up with his own farm, he abandoned the old ways. Instead of a mixed, diversified farm with rotating crops and fallow land, he embraced the new seed which had been created a few years earlier. They called it "Canola." You might not know, but there is no such thing as a Canola seed in nature. It was created from a rapeseed in a laboratory. It was supposedly healthier, but I've never trusted what people create in laboratories. I've never seen anything come out of those places that trumps the creation of God. I guess the best example of this is that genetically modified Canola that was introduced the year David sold the farm. It was created to resist herbicides so that farmers could pour chemicals onto their land to kill everything else but the Canola. Since the stuff is pollinated by the wind and spreads just about anywhere, it now grows everywhere—along the roadsides; in our backyards; and even in the cemeteries! It's a pest you can't kill anymore.

The year that David started to grow Canola, they had just declared it safe for human consumption in the U.S. He totally committed to it. Bought big equipment for its seeding and harvesting; didn't bother growing anything else; and year after year milked the land for a new crop of it. That's of course impossible if the soil cannot recover. So like the large agricultural companies taught him, David fumigated the soil, poured chemical fertilizers on it, and sprayed any pesticide and herbicide that was needed to protect his crop. When he got his piece of land from his parents, it was good, healthy, black dirt. It had lots of worms in it, and it smelled right. But after a few years of pouring all that crap on it, that soil was as dead as it could be. I once challenged David about this, "I bet you must have killed all the worms for miles by now. Pretty sure you couldn't find a single one anymore in your dirt."

"It's a Canola farm, not a worm farm, Ray," he replied. But in his eyes I could see it made him uncomfortable. He didn't really want to think about what he was doing to the land.

In order to make a return on all his expensive equipment, David leased other properties to farm, and over time expanded his own deeded land by buying that of his neighbors who had gone bankrupt. And there was always other land to purchase thanks to the corporate stranglehold on farmers.

You got to know that the big corporations not only used their influence by seducing farmers with promises of higher yields and better income through using their seeds and chemicals, but they also got the farmer on the other end when they purchased their crops. Our governments allowed companies to grow to virtual monopolies. Small and local cheese factories, slaughterhouses, grain mills, milk processing plants, leather tanners and wool processors all used to provide jobs to a widespread agricultural society. They were part of the fabric of farming communities that were spread across this country. One by one they were bought up by larger corporations which simply shut them down. And if that didn't work, those corporate lobbyists schemed with the government to complicate regulations so smaller companies couldn't comply and had to close down. This forced farmers to drive longer distances to sell their products, adding to their cost and reducing their negotiating power.

This voracious consolidation of food corporations led to our current situation, where only a handful of global companies control the world's food market. For the farmer this means that those corporations control the distribution of their produce and therefore set the price. And lo and behold, if we look at the numbers, we see that over the last few decades consumer food prices have been rising without interruption. Yet the farmer's revenue has been absolutely stagnant even though his costs have risen exponentially. And so this decline in a farmer's earnings has driven more and more farmers off the land and to the cities. It's been a deceitful corporate strategy driven by greed and sold to politicians as a necessity to increase food production. But it has come at the expense of destroying families, a sustainable agricultural way of life, food independence, the destruction of farming communities, and the growing pollution problem that ever larger cities carry with them.

I guess I'm ranting and you want me to talk about David, right? I heard on the news what David did in Sheridan. It did shock me. Even though I didn't like David, I never had any serious problems with him either. And even though I didn't approve of his methods, he did take care of his family once he returned from his travels. He was no troublemaker at that time. He even bought the chemicals from the company whose executives he shot.

And you know as far as I'm concerned, these big shots deserved it. I know that's probably not the politically correct thing to say. But I don't care. What they have done to our food, and to farming families and communities, is despicable.

My grandparents settled here from Europe. They came to this country to escape the lords and kings who owned the land and controlled the peasants' foods and crops. Now, look at what we have here. We don't have kings, emperors or barons but CEOs, the heads of corporate empires who decide the future for all of us now. Different name, but really the same thing. What gets to me is that all we do is say, "Yes, sir," and do as they say. And if they threaten for whatever reason to close down their operation or move it somewhere else, we even give them money so they will stay, and claim we do so in the name of the common good. Who are we fooling? The very freedom for which my parents moved here has been hijacked!

People today have no idea what democracy and freedom are about. Our ancestors didn't fight to get an empty right to vote, something that only leads to more regulations. Freedom is about less rules and regulations, and it is also about equality. It's not about putting on some more regulations and thinking we can control the beast we created. Regulating corporations is like controlling a patch of weed by putting a fence around it. It's never going to work. The pest will just keep on spreading. But what do we do? We build another fence around it, this time around a wider patch. We've been doing that now for more than a decade. It's simple, if you have weeds in your field, you've got to kill them, root them up, burn them, plow the field over—whatever it takes!—but you've got to do something that addresses the roots.

The problem is that when anyone speaks out against those giant corporations, the guys on television and radio make it sound like you're a communist. Suddenly you are against the free market. But I tell you, these megacorporations are the furthest thing from the free market. As a matter of fact, they have more in common with the central planning ideology of communism than with free entrepreneurship.

See, the problem isn't the ideology—it's simply sheer size. More than half of the largest economies in the world are now corporations, I heard. Well, that's the problem. They control too much! They gobble up all the competition and kill small entrepreneurs, just like they squeeze out the small family farmers here on the land. But the free market only works if there is healthy competition, if it's made up of small local businesses which together form a community. Nowadays, we're so blinded that we've even come to the point where many people feel we need those big corporations. People think that we depend on them. Can you imagine?

It's like with farmers who switched out our century-old proven farming methods of diversified farming and converted to monoculture. When something goes wrong, like a crop infestation or sickness, or a drop in market prices, it affects their entire income. If they manage to hang on despite their debt, they have their hands in their hair, unable to see a way out. But they fail to realize they own the land and soil! That's all they need to start growing other crops and develop a market in their local community.

The same happens in the cities. When a corporation shuts down or reduces its workforce, people don't know what to do anymore. They have forgotten that their value is in their hands, in their labor. Corporations are only using and often abusing that labor. People would be way better off and much more independent by running their own small businesses.

Corporations are just a screen for some rich people to hide behind. They're a tool for the new elite to control the world without being in the spotlight.

I didn't care much for David, but these guys he shot had it coming for a long time. If David hadn't done it, someone else would have at some point. What do you expect, that you can steal people's land? And their rights to work, food, shelter and clothing? That you can destroy their families and communities, herd them together in cities, enslave them through clever financial scams and poison their children, and that they're going to keep bending over without kicking back at one point? Yeah, those guys sure had it coming. When you spread your crap like that, sooner or later someone is going to be pissed off enough to do some real bad stuff.

DIARY OF JODY PALMER, DAVID'S WIFE.

December 20th, 1992.

Today was Tom's ninth birthday. He's growing up so fast. He's such a nice and good person. His heart overflows with love. He always puts people around him first, and when he enters a room his exuberance is infectious and impacts everyone in a positive way.

Needless to say his birthday party was a blast. David's parents and three of Tom's best friends came over. When I brought out the cake with the candles lit, Tessa—his best friend and little sister, who is now six—jumped up and down, pulling his arm while shouting, "Can I blow out the candles, Tom? Can I blow out the candles?"

Any other child would have felt they were being robbed of their moment of celebration. But not Tom; he smiled at his sister and said, "You can, Sis, but make sure you get them all so I can make a wish."

"What are you going to wish for?" Tessa asked with curiosity in her eyes.

"That next year, I'll be able to blow out my own candles," he grinned.

And so Tessa blew out Tom's birthday candles this year. The two are so adorable to see together. Even though his friends were there, Tom made sure that his sister was involved in their play.

Sometimes I wonder if Tom notices that David gives him much more attention than his little sister and tries to compensate for that. You see, David takes Tom everywhere with him. When David is on his tractor in the field, he'll come to the house to pick up Tom when school is over.

Tom loves riding the tractor with his father. Most of the time, I think it's good for both of them to have such quality time together. Except that day when David had taken Tom with him while spraying the field. What was he thinking, taking his son with him when fogging the land with chemicals? I was gone all day. We had a fight about it that night.

"You don't think I would put my son in any danger, do you?" David asked, insulted.

"No, I know you wouldn't do that, but those chemicals..."

"You're making too big a deal of it. They're safe. They are no more harmful than the salt you put in our food," he interrupted in defense.

"According to who? The people who sell them?" I questioned, in the hope of making him think.

"Everyone's using them. They're approved by the government. They've been tested and proven to be harmless in the quantities I use, and the produce on which I spray them is approved for human consumption. What more proof do you want?" he defended.

"Well, they can say what they want, but I don't want any of that stuff on the vegetables in our garden, and I certainly don't want my son in the tractor when you're spraying the field."

"Our son, you mean."

"Yes, our son. I don't want him near that stuff anymore!" I shouted in anger.

I knew though, that David hadn't meant anything bad. He adores Tom. He pours his heart and soul into his son.

I never brought this up with him, but I'm sure David's focus on Tom has to do with little Raul. To David, Tom is his chance for redemption. It's his chance to make up for what he wasn't able to give Raul in El Salvador—a true home, a father, safety, love and protection.

El Salvador has been on my mind again ever since the government there signed a peace accord with the rebels this past January. For years I hadn't thought about our time there. David and I have our own little family and farm now, and the responsibilities that have come along with that have kept me focused on the here and now.

But when El Salvador was in the news again and the same week another one of our neighbors decided to sell out since he couldn't keep the farm any longer, I pondered the parallels between what was happening here and the events David and I had witnessed down there.

Sure we don't have the kidnappings, oppression and murders here. But just like in El Salvador there's a systemic cleansing of the land under way. And it's using the same methodology, only more subtle.

In El Salvador the peasants were driven from the land through government land allocations or economic pressures that forced them to sell to the large landlords. Their goal was the creation of a large, cheap and mobile workforce, controlled by a small elite.

Just the same here, economic pressures, created by large multinational corporations—the paper weapons of the wealthy and powerful in this world—drive small family farmers from the land. And those who try to hang on have to deal with ever increasing government rules and regulations that are geared to get them to give it up. These events drive people to the cities, where they become part of the workforce that keeps the factories and offices of the rich elite operating.

What frightens me about the comparison is how the violence in El Salvador was unleashed. It started when the peasants challenged the status quo and demanded access to a bigger piece of the pie—a piece big enough so their families wouldn't starve. The only reason why this hasn't happened here is that the piece that's being given to the workers in this country allows them to feed their families. And the reality is that most people don't care about power, inequality or injustice, as long as they can feed their own family and see their children grow up in peace.

But what would happen here if the greedy get greedier and survival for the masses becomes a challenge? How quickly could our peaceful country erupt into similar violence when the elite feels threatened in their power position? The thought scares me and makes me realize we should never take our democratic powers and our peaceful society for granted. It's our obligation to defend it from the encroachment of powerful corporate rulers. It is our responsibility to defend our communities and to stand up for our neighbors. If we don't, who will stand up for us when we need help?

Seeing Tom's innocent generosity today was not only heartwarming, but it was also a reminder that as a parent I have a responsibility for the world in which my children are growing up. It struck me that such responsibility exceeds the simple provisions of food, clothing and shelter. It includes values, love and empathy. I realize that in our attempt to make a living as a farming family, both David and I have abandoned some of our values and lessons from our youth; things that were accentuated during our travels, but forgotten over time. The question for us to consider is what kind of legacy we leave behind for our children by abandoning our values and being acting puppets in a scheme that makes the rich richer and the poor poorer? What kind of world will we leave behind for them if we not only close our eyes, but act like victims without a choice, playing the game of dog-eat-dog? It's time for us to learn from our children, from their generosity and caring. It's time for us to live by example again and actively shape a world of community and love.

Kristen Smith, Environmentalist.

In January of 1994 my Canadian roommate and best friend from university called me up with an invitation for a presentation in her hometown of Maple Creek, Saskatchewan. We both had finished our Bachelors in Agricultural Chemistry the previous summer and decided to take a break from studying.

We had met during our first weeks of class, and discovered we both had the same motivation. This created an early alliance between us since it was in contrast to that of most of our classmates. Most students chose Agricultural Chemistry because they believed the problems of the world could be solved by chemical solutions to agricultural challenges. On the other hand, my friend and I had both been influenced by Rachel Carson's foundational environmental work, *Silent Spring.*

Man-made chemicals were the cause of a lot of damage in the world, a harm of which we only had limited knowledge. The problem with understanding the consequences of chemical applications was the lack of independent scientific research. Most environmental and health impact analyses are commissioned by the corporations who are producing the chemicals—companies that have, of course, an obvious financial benefit from positive study results. And as there are no immediate economic benefits in studying health and environmental risks of applied chemicals, hardly any funds are available to finance such independent research. Slowly though, more and more information surfaces as non-profit groups allocate funds to examine these risks.

My friend and I chose our field of study because we wanted to contribute to the unmasking of the ugly chemical truth and explore ways of using non-intrusive chemistry according to a biological model. A chemistry that would not pollute but rather function independently from nature in a closed loop, or else be based on natural biological processes (what's now called bio-mimicry).

My friend's mother was somewhat of an activist herself. She was the kind of woman who cared deeply about the community she lived in. When it was being threatened, she was a person who stood up to protect it. A few years ago she had been instrumental in rallying the entire Maple Creek community when the school board closed the historic Jasper School and wanted to level the turn-of-the-century building. They ended up buying the 1910 building for ten dollars and received grant money to convert it into a historical museum.

More recently, my friend's mother had heard there was a higher occurrence of childhood cancers in agricultural communities. Now she had taken on the cause of educating the community on the subject. She had organized an information evening on the twenty-first of April about the health risks and impact of agricultural chemicals, and had railroaded her daughter into making the presentation. My friend had called on me for help. She was more of an introverted type, and had never felt comfortable in talking before large groups. On the other hand, I was the extrovert—probably another reason why we complemented each other well. I thrived on crowds and loved to take people on an educational journey.

And so on that Thursday afternoon in April I arrived in the small rural community of Maple Creek on the Canadian prairies. The presence of towering grain terminals gave away the community's agricultural orientation.

My friend had asked me to meet with her at Curry's Bakery. Her directions led me via a street parallel to the railroad past the historic Colonial Hotel. A left turn and I reached my destination. The aroma of freshly baked bread greeted me as I entered the establishment.

My friend met me with a smile and a hug. Over coffee and a piece of pie, we caught up with each other at one of the retro-styled small dining tables in the front part of the store.

Towards the evening we headed to the Armoury community hall, a red brick historic building with two-story-high walls in which the builder forgot to place windows until just before putting up the roof. The hall still had the Spartan look one would expect from old army barracks. I felt like Alice in Wonderland guided by a mysterious invisible hand, from my home town in the Black Hills of South Dakota to this red-walled vestige of the Armoury in this prairie community, to unveil the ugly truth about the dangers of chemicals on the farm and to explore hopeful alternatives. It was fairytale-like, and so was the love story that commenced there.

I remember it like yesterday, the first time I laid eyes on David, even though nothing special happened between us. My friend and I were organizing our overhead slides. The hall was filling up with people. Once in a while I would look up to give a friendly nod to the arriving audience. At one such moment, David was there, a tall, not particularly handsome, but strong farmer. He walked with comfort and ease. When he returned my welcoming smile, his eyes gave a glimpse of inquisitiveness, gentleness and determination. I hesitated, captured by the moment, unable to understand why this man felt so familiar. And where did the sudden warm energy in my belly come

from?   I forced myself to concentrate on the business at hand.   It
wasn't the right time to feel such things; I had a job to do.   I watched
the hall fill up, all the way to the back.

Here were farmers, the people who provide our bread in the
morning, put food on our plates day after day, men and women who
raise children and have dreams for them; who love the land and are
raised to respect and steward it with patience and gratitude.   But just
like with factory workers or miners across the globe, to white-
collared executives in faraway board rooms they were resources to be
employed in a game of commerce in which the money-making end
justifies the means.   Often these people were ignorant of the dangers
and consequences of their work with regard to their own health, and
that of their families.   It was my task that night to open a window to
those risks without leaving people in hopeless despair or blaming the
victims of this tragedy.   Instead I wanted to empower farmers and
their families to consciously reclaim control over their lives and
transform their agricultural methods to maintain healthy families,
communities, consumers and land.

My friend's mother introduced the topic of the evening.
Then she gave the floor to me.

I started by reading the Laws of Ecology from Ernest
Callenbach.   Four simple lines that capture the essence of how our
natural world works, and something I thought most people in the
room would relate to:

"All things are interconnected.

Everything goes somewhere.

There is no such thing as a free lunch.

Nature bats last."

I paused, glanced over the room, noticed the nods and felt
content with how I had captured the audience's attention.   During the

forty minutes that followed I took people on a journey through some history of agriculture.

Together we remembered how as hunter-gatherers we became farmers so we could settle and create a more secure life for our families. We remembered how for millennia the mixed family farm had been the center point of society. We remembered how throughout the ages a small elite group of warriors and self-appointed landlords had presumptuously elevated themselves from agricultural life to lay claim to part of the produce in a form of legalized robbery. We remembered how farmers quietly paid those tributes so they would be left alone and could raise their families while the lords went in pursuit of power and control with their games of war. We remembered how initially land titles were not that important, since all land was common land, owned by the collective or by an individual, but something to which all commoners had certain traditional rights like farming, hunting, collecting firewood and use as grazing land. We remembered how the enclosure of private land, accelerated by the industrialization of the textile industry in England, marked the end of the land commons and drove the commoners from the land to make room for wool-producing sheep. We remembered how this created the vast mass of landless people who could be employed as cheap labor in plantations and factories. We remembered how after World War I nitrogen fertilizers were pushed onto agriculture to offload the stockpiles for the production of bombs. We remembered how this transformed diversified agriculture into monocultures and eliminated the need to give the soil time to recuperate and replenish through crop rotation and fallow land practices. We remembered how at the end of World War II the industrial elite decided to sell the large leftover stockpiles of nerve gas to farmers to kill insects. We remembered how this unleashed the war on the land with the production of a multitude of toxic pesticides, herbicides and fungicides that kill any possible disease, weed or fungus. We remembered how our governments allowed food companies to concentrate in ever larger corporations, effectively killing the free market and handing the reins of the world's food production to a handful of corporate giants. We remembered how those corporate giants increased their control over our food supply by claiming ownership over our seed—the very essence of life—through patenting and intellectual property rights. We remembered how we used to save our seeds, but are now forced to buy them year after year from the seed companies. We remembered how the giant food corporations waged war on the family farm by using their market muscle to pay less for farmers' crops while charging more for the seeds and chemicals the farmers needed. We remembered how for decades the retail prices for food have exponentially increased. We remembered how farm accidents once were the farmers' leading cause of death, but now have been replaced by suicides fuelled by financial stress and indebtedness. We remembered how we used to raise our farm animals under the open sky with respect, but now massive industrial complexes, using antibiotics and hormones to optimize production yields, disregard the animals' rights to a humane life. We remembered the vibrant agricultural communities of old which are, one by one, transformed into ghost towns as the industrialization of our land steadily progresses, adding farmers to the landless masses to be employed in industrial factories. We remembered how we all sat on the sidelines and let it all happen.

The mood in the room was somber. This wasn't a fairytale story, and sugarcoating it didn't benefit anyone. I knew it was about to get worse before I could turn the corner and pick people up to empower them.

I repeated Callenbach's words: "All things are interconnected. Everything goes somewhere. There is no such thing as a free lunch. Nature bats last." I paused. The audience was thinking about those words again. They knew where this was leading.

"Here's what we know so far about our chemical legacy," I continued. "Every year we are spraying some three million tons of agricultural chemicals on our earth. Every year those chemicals kill over fifty million American birds. Killer whales have washed up on shores and needed to be treated as toxic waste due to their PCB contamination. As a matter of fact, scientists are practically unable to find any living creatures free of chemical contamination. Chemicals have been found in fish in remote mountain lakes; in earthworms, birds and their eggs; and yes, in the human body as well."

I wanted this part of the presentation to end. It was like confronting people with a nightmare that was only too real. "These chemicals have now been related to a myriad of diseases," I ploughed on. "Among them are several forms of cancer, Parkinson's, auto-immune diseases and nervous system disorders. Our children are the most vulnerable, particularly those in agricultural communities."

A murmur of anger and fear went through the hall. The eyes of the farmer who had attracted my attention earlier that evening were locked onto me. In them I saw concern, but also disbelief and a glimpse of anger.

Then I dropped the bomb. "Farmers' children have double the risk of developing childhood leukemia," I said, and then presented the results of a recent study that compared children of two similar Mexican villages with the same type of genetics, food consumption, education and economy but with one notable difference: one village was located in the mountain foothills far away from agricultural land, and the other was a farming community where herbicides and pesticides were so heavily sprayed that even once-common insects had almost entirely disappeared from the environment. The results were frightening. Women in the agricultural community had high levels of pesticides in the umbilical cords of their unborn children, as well as in their breast milk. In comparison to the foothills community, the children in the farming village had difficulty with hand-eye coordination and poorer memory skills; were prone to more aggressive behavior; and were less sociable and creative while playing.

"How did we ever buy into the myth that it was a good idea to grow more food by using poison?" I concluded the horror story.

"But here's the good news," I said. "You can choose to change! Consumers are waking up to what is happening to their food supply. They want quality and healthy produce. There are organic farmers who have shown how you can make a living while saying 'no' to agricultural chemicals. There are others who have diversified and added value delivering end-food products for consumers. Both farmers and artisan food producers increase their margins by selling direct to consumers at farmers' markets, rebuilding the sustainable economic model of local economies again. You have the power to change things!"

I was waiting for some sign of relief from the crowd, but none came.

"Young woman, how old are you?" a gray-haired farmer asked.

"Twenty-three."

"Did you grow up on a farm, or is this only book knowledge?" he challenged.

"I did grow up on a ranch near the Black Hills in South Dakota," I responded matter-of-factly, but a little agitated by the line of questioning which seemed to attempt to discredit me rather than concentrate on the facts and issues I had presented. "My parents raised hormone-free cattle and sustainably grown hay."

"So how did they fare?" the farmer continued.

I hesitated while sadness squeezed my throat with the memories of a life long gone. "My parents lost the ranch when I was thirteen. I remember sitting on the top rail of the corral as they were loading the cattle on the transport trucks, and the cows' mournful calling for the calves. It was then I realized my connection to the country and the importance of standing up and protecting this way of life."

"Your father should have sprayed. He might still be around!" the farmer sneered.

"You mean, at the expense of my health?" I snapped back, this time visibly agitated.

The man who had attracted my attention earlier that evening came to my rescue by shifting the nature of the conversation.

"If we don't take our wives and children with us in our fields, or take them there only some time after spraying, would that reduce their risk?"

Finally a question that brought us back on topic.

"Good question," I encouraged him. "The further you keep your family away from those chemicals, the better. But research has shown that pesticides drift into houses via dust. It also enters your home attached to boots, shoes and pets."

From then on the community explored the viability of diversified and organic farming and developing a local market for their produce. For every idea, there were at least ten problems raised. This certainly wasn't going to be an easy journey for them, but at least they were trying. The message got through: they might survive economically with conventional farming but it came at a cost—one they weren't prepared to pay.

When it was all over and people were leaving the hall, the farmer who kept fascinating me came over.

"Hi, I'm David," he said as he offered a spade of a hand. My knees trembled, my stomach glowed and my chest tightened up. All these were things I had felt before when I had been in love. "Was this love at first sight?" I asked myself. I had never believed in it, but I was converted that day. I felt an inexplicable, almost carnal, attraction to this mature farmer whom I guessed was at least ten years older than me. My only trouble was that there was no sign those feelings were mutual.

That evening though, the world seemed to disappear as I submerged in conversation with this all-too-familiar stranger. At first he wanted to know more about the research I had talked about. He was genuinely concerned, but he kept his cool and didn't panic about all the bad news either. Then I felt special as he wanted to know more about me. He wanted to know where I lived, how I had come to know my friend, and what happened after my parents sold the ranch. As I enjoyed the attention of this attractive man, I flirted with him, and thought he did so too. But what man doesn't respond affectionately to a younger woman's charming advances?

It was only when I started asking questions about him that I realized David was already in love. He was in love with his wife. Instead of sharing things about himself, he kept on talking about her.

Strangely enough, it didn't diminish my feelings for him; it only made this charismatic man even more alluring. Here was a guy clearly committed to his wife, and I glowed in his presence and cherished the attention he gave me. What was I getting myself into? I cursed myself for always falling in love with the wrong men—well, I guess not really the wrong men, but men who were beyond my reach. Before he left me that night, David invited me to his house to meet his family the following day. I accepted.

Just before noon the next day I drove through a large pole gate decorated with a set of elk antlers over the top. The driveway led through open fields to what looked like a vestige of green trees—the traditional prairie shelterbelt that provided a home protection from the polar winds and harsh prairie winters. At the center of the green oasis an old farmhouse with a traditional porch and swing was waiting for me. A set of metal grain bins next to a large metal shop on the side stood in stark contrast to the heritage character of the home. The shelterbelt and restored wooden home spoke of harmony, wisdom and balance, about time-learned lessons, about the cycle of life and death and of the perseverance of the human spirit to realize a dream. The metal of the shop and grain bins was shiny, almost arrogant; it was hard and cold. It was what we called progress, but progress to what?

I pulled up in front of the house and just as I reached the porch the door swung open. An all-natural woman—no make-up, no fancy clothing, and hair stuck together behind her head—greeted me with the warmest smile, eyes that spoke of kindness, and a young girl attached to her leg. "Hi, I'm Jody. Glad you could make it out for a visit. David told me how interesting your presentation was last night. I wish I could have been there. But one of us had to stay home with the children."

It was the first time I had met David's family. When I left that day I thought it to be the last. Seeing how happy they were, how much Jody and David loved each other, and how the children were raised in a joyful environment but also with a sense of global consciousness would help me to comprehend the hardship and loss David endured in the years that followed.

That afternoon over some delicious home-cooked quiche we shared our tales. Jody wanted to know all about the research I had presented the previous evening and the impact of the farm chemicals on her children. We bounced off solutions like organic farming and local foods, and their challenges in a harsh northern climate such as theirs. I shared with both of them why I entered this field of study and my ambition to make this world a better place.

They surprised me with their story of their time in El Salvador. "I haven't talked about this for years," David confided, "but for some reason I feel compelled to share it with you."

"David doesn't often talk with others about it," Jody explained. "It's so difficult to explain to people who've never traveled through a developing country. But between the two of us it's a regular topic of conversation. We've observed the same conquest for control of land play out here in North America as well. It's more subtle; people aren't shot or tortured, but they're robbed of their lifestyle and livelihood just the same.

"The signing of the North American Free Trade Agreement and the uprising of the Zapatista movement in Mexico in January this year reminded us of how the age-old battle for land control is still alive and gets fought with whatever means possible. Nowadays, though, those who already control vast stretches of the world are also setting the rules and creating the laws which allow them to accelerate their plans on a global scale with paper contracts, and use police and armies to enforce their continual land grab."

"It's mind-boggling!" David added, "You would think that the Zapatista struggle for work, land, food, health care, education, independence, liberty, democracy, justice and peace shouldn't be a struggle at all, but rather be the foundation of any democracy, or any nation with which we enter into a trade agreement."

"It's that nasty World Trade Organization," I chimed in, "and their Structural Adjustment Program which is a condition for countries entering trade agreements like NAFTA. It demands that all common lands be privatized so that big corporations can take control of them, and simultaneously calls for a reduction in health care and education and demands a focus on export-oriented industries. In essence it's asking the country to give up its sovereignty to line the pockets of the global elite who're the only ones to benefit from this."

My passion got the best of me, and I added, "What happened to the principles of democracy—by the people for the people—and what happened to justice when international laws and trade agreements favor the few at the cost of the many? Glad someone stood up and took up the fight. Maybe that's what's missing to make a lasting change; maybe we need more Zapatistas around the world."

I remember to this day the sadness I saw in both Jody's and David's eyes when they looked at each other in response to my words. It was a deep-felt grief, not for a particular event, but for the state of the human condition and the cruelty of man against fellow human beings, against people with brothers, sisters, fathers, mothers, sons and daughters—all people with dreams, and all in search of happiness.

David broke the silence. "I'm not sure if violence is the solution," he said. "I'm not sure if it ever can be. It sure didn't solve much in El Salvador. It only caused a lot of bloodshed.

"Jody and I went to see the movie, *Schindler's List*, last month. How can one human being bring himself to slaughter others by the millions, like they did with the Jews during World War II? And you know what's the scariest of all?"

David paused here, his look intensified, and I shrugged my shoulders in response.

"The scariest thing is that those who lived through it will all be dying over the next two decades. And then who will remember what happened?"

"I will."

An innocent but serious, soft-spoken voice came from the corner of the room. It was Tom. He and his sister had been quietly playing while we were having our conversation. It was the only time I met Tom, but the depth of thought of this young boy gave me hope, hope for a future where people would care for each other. "We learned in school about Anne Frank's letters," he explained. "I will remember, Daddy!" he stressed.

"Thank you, son," David said. "And you know, we have to act as well, so such things won't happen anymore." He turned to me again and continued, "Sadly, it seems that even now when we all remember what happened to the Jews, we don't find it in our hearts to act when hundreds of thousands of Tutsis are being massacred in Rwanda because our politicians argue about whether this should be called genocide or not!"

Sadness poured from his face as he shook his head in disbelief. He stood up and put his hands on Tom's shoulders. "See this big guy," he said. "Tom has his eye on the Maple Creek hockey team, the Hawks. You should see him skate; he'll be the next Gretzky." And with that David changed the subject to things closer to home, things that were tangible, brought joy and helped him to forget the cruelty of the world we live in.

When I left that afternoon, I was still in love even though there was no doubt as to whom David's heart belonged. To make my feelings manageable and save my heart's torture, I decided on two things: I wasn't going to seek out any further contact with David, and whenever I thought of him I would do so with the love for the brother I never had.

And so our most peculiar relationship started. Little did I know how things would change a few years later.

Eva Green, David's Mother.

The moment is engraved on my soul. Friday morning, December twenty-second, 1994, two days after Tom's eleventh birthday. I was baking bread for his birthday party the following day. I felt blessed on that winter morning; my hands were covered in dough, and as I looked out of the kitchen window I admired the sunlight's dance on the snow crystals blanketing the fields. That was until the phone rang and I heard David's distressed voice.

"Mom, I have bad news."

My son paused; he couldn't say what he had to say. My throat squeezed tight.

"Tom has cancer. He's got leukemia."

The words rang in my head. This wasn't possible. My grandson was only eleven. He was a star player on the Hawks Peewee hockey team. He was a healthy, strong child; the sweetest boy ever. There must have been a mistake.

After a long silence and with fear in my voice I asked, "Are you sure? Doctors can make mistakes, you know."

"I know, Mother, it's a hard thing to accept, but it's true. Tom has cancer."

That day, the world as I knew it came to an end. Things would never be the same anymore. No more joyful worriless feasts with my two grandchildren competing for my undivided attention.

No more exciting hockey games to cheer on my dear Tom. No more comforting hugs without wondering if this would be the last time I'd feel the warmth of his tiny hands in his innocent and loving embrace.

The weeks leading up to that day, Tom had felt tired and complained about muscle aches. When he couldn't perform in hockey practice, had no energy at any time, and cried to stay home when he had a game to play, Jody had taken him to see a doctor, not really expecting anything serious. We all thought it was part of his hormones kicking in; you know, growing pains and the bodily exhaustion of rapid physical growth. The doctor's office had taken blood as part of their examination. That morning the results had come in.

After I went through the initial shock, my maternal instincts took over. I had to be there for my son and Jody, and of course for little Tom. In truth, I had to be there for them to keep myself occupied and safe from my own grief.

Within twenty-four hours Tom was checked into the hospital in Regina for surgery. They checked his bone marrow for cancer cells, and did a spinal tap to check the spinal fluid for the same bad stuff. Next was the chemo treatment. It would take a minimum of three years, and Tom could be sterile at the end of it. David and Jody were also told their son would have to be home-schooled for the rest of the year.

The good news: My grandson had a seventy percent chance of beating the cancer. And so that's what we focused on. When the doctors commenced their treatment to heal Tom, I prayed daily to God and asked Him to save our little boy.

Christmas that year took place in the hospital. We put up a little tree in Tom's room and tried as best as we could to make it a cheerful time under the shadow of the thought that this could be our last Christmas together.

On January third there was good news: Tom was responding well to the treatment. A chemo and drug treatment program was put together. Jody and David were warned about the side effects; hair loss and nausea. But they had no idea how their lives would be turned upside down during the year that followed. There were daily trips to the Maple Creek hospital for IVs and other chemo treatments, several blood tests a week, numerous painful bone marrow aspirations, antibiotics to avoid pneumonia and other bacterial infections since both the cancer and the treatment destroyed Tom's immune system, and more. Life suddenly was something that happened on the periphery of Tom's treatment plan.

But there was a silver lining. There was a seventy percent chance that Tom would recover, and he was responding well.

With the prospect of death—of permanent loss—we value life so much more and go out of our way to show our love. And so we cherished each day that Tom was with us. We were grateful for every second we had together.

I visited my grandson daily. "Someone has to give Jody some relief," I told people, but in truth, I simply wanted to get my share of Tom's presence. Do my part, give him my love, be comforted by his smile. Oh, yes, he still smiled. Apart from the times when the chemo made him really sick, he accepted his condition with a graceful ease.

On the other hand, Jody carried fear in her eyes on an ongoing basis. She struggled to enjoy Tom's fleeting presence for fear of what might come. And David had become strong as a rock; he carried Tom in his arms to and from the hospital, time and time again. David was determined to save his son, no matter what. It was a determination grounded in his failure to save a little boy in El Salvador and in his feelings of guilt because of the chemicals he had sprayed on his fields.

Tessa didn't really understand. She knew her brother was really sick, but eight-year-old children cannot comprehend death, or the threat of death. At times I felt sorry for her since she almost disappeared into the shadows with all the attention going to Tom. I made a point of giving her an extra cuddle once in a while. It was heart-warming though to see how tenderly she tried to comfort Tom when he didn't feel well, and how throughout his illness Tom kept taking care of Tessa. He would make sure we didn't forget about his little sister!

In the face of death we spent much more time together as a family. We learned to listen better during that period, not only to Tom, but to each other——to understand each other without trying to force our expectations onto one another, and certainly not onto Tom. We played a lot of board games and took any opportunity to create some joy in little Tom's life. A smile was all we were after; it was our reward for a day well-lived.

One day in the fall, after an afternoon of board games and laughter, I hugged him before going home. His embrace was more intense than usual. When he let go, he held onto my hands and said, "If I go to heaven before you, Nanny, I'll ask God to keep an open seat for you next to me. I want you to sit next to me in heaven."

I choked up; I couldn't say a word more. Tears welled up in my eyes and I hugged him like it was our last time.

For almost a year, Tom did well, seemingly making progress. Then for some unknown reason, he relapsed in late November of 1995.

Diary of Jody Palmer, David's Wife.

Tuesday, January 23, 1996.

I just returned from seeing my little boy. I wasn't sure if I would be strong enough to see him, but then I really wanted to. I had to see him one more time, engrave his face into my soul. Already I was afraid of how the memory might fade with time.

He was so pretty. Nicely dressed. He was still skinny; there was no way to hide his weight loss of the last few months. But he had his color back and a soft smile on his face. When I touched his hand, the illusion faded. His hand was cold as ice; my little boy was dead. My little Tom lost his fight to leukemia this past Saturday, January twentieth, in the darkness of that moonless night. David tried to comfort me when he led me home from the morgue, but he couldn't. There's no comfort for the pain of a mother who loses her child. If anything, David's strength is what I needed, because if I hadn't been able to hold onto his arm, I surely would have collapsed next to the coffin of my boy.

Who am I writing this for? I always thought my journal might be read some day by my children. But only one is left now, and who knows when she might be taken from me next. This was supposed to be my story through time for my children; maybe now it can reach you, my son, through space.

Dear Tom, going forward, this writing is for you.

The past three days I cried endlessly. I remembered your birth, your first bubble bath, your first birthday and when you took your first steps. I remembered how you cared for just about everyone around you, how your little heart radiated so much love and acted like a magnet for people to enjoy your presence.

As I'm writing this, I'm looking at a blurry picture of you. Your kiss to me, framed in time. I don't really care that it's not focused; it is you, your kiss for me, that's what counts.

You were three when I bought you the Polaroid camera. I was curious to have a glimpse of the world through your eyes. You took pictures of your toys, but also of your feet, Daddy's tractor, Daddy and me, the Canola that sprouted in the field, every insect you saw, and pictures of your newborn sister—lots. Pictures of her hands, her cute face and her little toes. One evening before you went to sleep you gave me a hug, then got all excited. You grabbed your camera and focused it on yourself and said, "This kiss is for you, Mommy." Now I'm so glad to have your kiss frozen in time.

Those memories are the only sparkle of light that can warm my heart. In their absence my heart is as cold as your hand I touched in the morgue.

I know you were ready to go last week, but I wasn't. I don't think any mother can ever be ready for her child to leave this world before she does.

It was touching how even in your last days your heart went out to your sister. I know I didn't answer you because I was too emotional when you asked, "Mommy, when I'm gone, who will be there to play with Tessa and look after her? Mommy, please take good care of her; she needs your hugs, and wants to ride the tractor with Daddy."

I promise you, my son, that I will make every effort to give her extra hugs and spend more time playing with her. I've already done so over the last few days to honor your wish, but it's so hard; I do it, but I don't feel anything. It scares me and floods me with guilt. I should feel something when I hug my baby daughter when she doesn't understand why her older brother and playmate doesn't come home anymore. But my heart is dead; only my body is going through the motions. I'll do my best to keep this promise to you, but I'm at a loss how to love with a heart that's empty and cold.

It feels like the world around me is separated from me. My soul belongs to the past, and my heart finds comfort only in my memories of you. And each time the world out there pulls me away from a memory, the only thing I feel is pain, raw agonizing waves of pain.

The tears are impossible to stop. They well up, like the ocean is breathing waves onto the shore of my heart. The grief engulfs me, and just like the waves, it pulls back, but only enough to feel the raw wound caused by the emptiness you've left behind in this world; then the next wave takes over. My tears breathe out the pain in a continual attempt to cleanse my heart. But I don't feel the washing, there is no cleansing. I only feel the sandiness of grit, the abrasiveness of pain, that raw wound that keeps bleeding when the wave pulls back. A wound left behind when my heart was robbed of the color of this world.

I keep asking myself why—why you? Why did God decide to take you away from me? But I know there's no answer. I know I should accept this, but I cannot. How do I live in a world without color? How do I love with an empty and cold heart? How do I function in a world which cannot reach my soul?

I'm glad I can reach you, my little Tom, through these words. I know you can hear me, and that's what gives me comfort. Some day, in another place, we will be together again. Then once more, we will be a family.

LETTER FROM DAVID TO HIS SON.

Sunday, January 28ᵗʰ, 1996.

Dear Tom,

Just like the day you were born, it's the end of a long day, a day that in the darkness of night became the next day's morning. It's after midnight, early Sunday morning, and I'm writing you again. You'll never read this letter, like you'll never read the letter I wrote you when you were born twelve years ago. I was planning to give it to you when you turned eighteen. I'd never imagined you wouldn't reach that age. I'm still writing you as I'd like to think you can hear me. It's like the writing etches my words in time and space.

Today we laid you to rest. I'm so sorry, my son. I'm so terribly sorry that I didn't take better care of you, that I wasn't able to save you. I'm not sure I'll ever be able to forgive myself.

A long time ago, in a country called El Salvador, I let another boy down—a boy your age, a boy who depended on me, a boy I failed to save from the greed-driven violent world around us. At that time I had never felt so powerless in my life. I walked away from Raul justifying to myself that this was not my fight, it wasn't my country, and he wasn't my son. Disgusted with a world which not only values money and gold over the well-being of our children, but is actually prepared to sacrifice our children for the almighty dollar, I tried to hide from it, ignore it, lay low and not ruffle any feathers. I ignored the ugliness and wrongs in the world, the unjustness of the system, and the hypocrisy of our society, and I focused on simply raising a family and taking care of my wife and children. I embraced a world that values paper contracts and money, but doesn't value life. I surrendered to a world of living paper and dying hearts. And look where it got me.

Never have I been more wrong.

The truth is, when I saw injustice in El Salvador, I turned the other way, walked away when things got hot, because I simply didn't have the guts to fight. I couldn't see how the oppression in that country was related to my life, how Raul's life was interconnected with mine, how the fight of his people was also my fight.

Now I've paid the price. I've paid for my horrible mistake, for my deliberate ignorance and cowardice, with your life—my son's life. To make matters worse, my choice to deny the obvious wrongs have made me an accomplice in your death. It was I who sprayed those chemicals onto our fields, the very poisons that made you sick. Had I stood up for a better world, had I acted with conscience, you'd still be alive.

How on earth could we so lose our way, lose our connection with the land that nurtures all creatures on this planet? How could we ever decide to wage war on it with the very poisons that were developed to kill people in heartless wars? Are we really that stupid? Is it too difficult to understand that everything in nature goes somewhere and sooner or later ends up back on our plates? Someday we will eat our trash and our poison; it's an unavoidable result of being on top of the food chain. Maybe we often don't act because the victims are other people's children, and maybe we stay quiet in the hope of protecting our own—that is, until the day when it's our family's turn to be the victim. And that day, we wake up to our own deceit and guilt. I'm so sorry, my boy, that I didn't wake up sooner; that I didn't at least try to make this world a better and healthier place for you instead of considering the sacrifices of my own comfort.

When we drove home from the hospital the night you left us, only the wailing cries of your mother broke the silent darkness. The roads around us were empty, and inside our car, time stood still.

But there was this one vehicle that came from the opposite direction which made me realize that time outside of our experience was moving on. At that point, despite the weight of my guilt, I realized I had a choice. I could feel sorry for myself, let sorrow engulf me and paralyze my life, or I could use your life and death as my guide to do something that gives value to your life as well as your death; I could do something that honors the way you crossed my path. I could use your memory to inspire me to do what I failed to do for you and Raul. I could use your memory to make things better for other boys and girls like you. Your legacy could live on through my actions.

I'll carry my cross, but I will not surrender in self-pity. Instead, I will use it to gain the strength I didn't have years earlier when I left Raul behind.

I'm not sure how things work where you are now, my dear Tom. I hope you can hear me. But if there is anything you can do for your mother, to ease her pain and give her comfort, to help her find the strength to live through your loss, then please do so. I'm really concerned about her. Your death has broken her heart, sucked the life from her soul and made her unable to feel anything but your loss. And if I'm worthy, please help her to forgive me for my trespasses. I promised her when we left El Salvador that I would never let anything bad happen to our children. I failed you, and I failed her.

Laying you to rest today was the hardest thing we ever had to do in our lives. I'm sure it's the hardest thing for any parent to go through.

While your mother could only sob, I wanted to make your funeral meaningful—let it be a closure of one chapter and an opening of another; a celebration of your life, but also a start of your living legacy. I asked the priest to read some words from Monsignor Romero, words that I hope would seed some good from your death: "I call upon all of you creators of so many families, builders of so many homes, that each family in El Salvador does not become an obstacle to the urgent changes that society needs. That no one family, to be well on its own, isolates itself from the whole society. No one marries only for the two of them to be happy; marriage has a great social function, it must be a torch that lights up its surroundings and other couples' paths to other liberations. From the family must come men and women able to promote the changes that are necessary in politics, in society, in the paths to justice; changes that will not occur if families oppose them."

I had chosen a song from Bruce Springsteen to be played upon leaving the church. It was released about the same time as your relapse. The song was about the ghost of Tom Joad, and the words could not have been more relevant for me. I'm glad the priest agreed to play the song. Otherwise I'm not sure I would have been able to step behind your little coffin without collapsing under the agonizing grief. My feet felt like lead, the walk behind your coffin the longest road I'd ever walked. The loss, the pain, was taking hold of me. But then I heard the words of the song from the ghost of Tom Joad, and I imagined those words to be yours directed to me. I felt the strength returning to my legs. I had a mission, and as it crystallized it gave me strength to take another step, and then another, and another. And as the words of the song kept ringing through my head, your voice came through and said: "Dad, wherever a farmer loses his farm, wherever we spray death on our soil, wherever living paper wins over dying hearts, open your eyes, Dad, it's me you see."

EVA GREEN, DAVID'S MOTHER.

When Tom died, I didn't only lose my beloved grandson, I lost my entire family. Tom's death delivered a blow to David and Jody from which they couldn't recover. I had my own grief, but didn't have the luxury to mourn. In a way, that was good; it allowed time to do its wonderful work for me. Not that it ever makes the loss, that gnawing pain, go away, but it takes the edge off. It puts us in a position of acceptance and realization that life is bigger than we are and that it's not up to us to try to figure out God's plan. We can only be grateful for those who pass through our lives.

Tom's death struck Jody's heart with such force that she was never able to heal, to discover life beyond her pain and loss. She was unable to open a door that allowed light to return to her heart; Tom had taken all her love into his grave. She didn't show any desire to try to fill her heart again. The sparkling, dynamic young woman now only sobbed, day in and day out. She didn't want to get up in the morning and didn't open the curtains of her room to let in the sunlight.

We tried to encourage her—"You've got to be strong for Tessa." But to no avail. Day by day, she drowned further in her sorrow. The only time I saw fire and energy in her eyes was the day that I opened Tom's room and wanted to start cleaning it out. It was something that was difficult enough for me as it was, but I thought doing so might help Jody to see beyond the past. I remember walking into the room—a relic, left just like it was the day he died, only with more dust on the worldly things that surrounded my grandson in life. I had brought a cardboard box with me to put some of his belongings in.

Tom's hockey jersey still hung in the closet, but the boy who fit inside it was missing. In silence I cried on Tom's bed with the jersey in my arms until I finally found the strength to load up the box. The jersey I hung back in the closet.

When I walked out of the room with Tom's things in my hands, Jody was standing right in front of me.

"Don't you think about wiping out the memories of my son!" she hissed. "You're not going to erase Tom from this house."

I wanted to reason with her; it had been six months since his death. But I remembered how I had just wept on his bed, and I wasn't going to test the ferocity I could read in Jody's eyes. I put the box back, closed the door and hugged her while we cried together.

Poor little Tessa had to deal with her own loss—that of her older brother and playmate; that of the boy who always took care of her. She would cry silently, but no solace would come from her mother. So, I more or less ended up living in my son's house.

I spent much time with Tessa during those months following Tom's death. I comforted her when she was sad, played with her when she was looking for a friend, and got her ready for school in the morning once she was ready for class again.

I tried to get Jody up, to take her for a walk in the fields, to get her to talk about just anything. But I failed, at least most of the time. The few times she did get up, her eyes were broken, her gaze empty and her face without any sign of feeling. She had become a walking corpse. The few times she did speak shocked me the most. The tone of her voice was one of cold and utter resignation. Jody had abandoned all desire to live.

I felt for David; I could tell he struggled not only with Tom's loss, but also with his feelings of guilt. I told him not to be so hard on himself, but he didn't want to hear that from me. Instead he insisted on acknowledging his guilt and using it as fuel for growth and better future decisions.

"Ignoring my fault doesn't change the outcome; it only gives me reason not to change. By recognizing my complicity, I must change, do things better, and maybe if I'm worthy God will give me another chance to make a difference for another young boy at some other place and in some other time. I'm not sure how to change things yet, and don't really want to think or talk about it now."

David did heal his heart, or so it seemed, even though he refused to talk about the events. He coped by moving on with life. At first I thought he was too quick; that he hadn't taken enough time to mourn. But when I saw him with Jody, I knew he'd be fine. He took such tender care of her, undeterred by her depressed condition. He gave her all his love; he did so even for years after the event, without ever expecting that any of his love would be returned. David knew Jody's heart was encapsulated by a cold shell, her inner beauty trapped inside and her love unable to reach the outside world. And just like with Tom's death, David took the burden upon himself. He had chosen to pay for his mistakes, and cared for Jody unconditionally until the end of their days.

Tessa finally did get to ride David's tractor as he focused his fatherly love on his daughter to compensate for the motherly love that was stolen from her.

Nine months passed, and the numbness in the family had become the everyday norm. Then one day after harvesting, David came in from the fields, walked into the kitchen and spoke with a resoluteness that was vaguely familiar. It was one I hadn't heard since Tom had gotten sick.

"Mother, I'm sorry, but we're moving. There's simply too much here that reminds me of Tom. I can't get myself to change his room, and even if I were to get to that point, I would still see him playing on the floor in the corner of the kitchen, dragging Tessa to her room or running to me through the field to join me in the tractor. I can't change the room or the memories, but I can move and start over. Besides, I'll never use chemicals on the land anymore, and this harvest has proven I can't produce a profitable yield without fertilizers and pesticides in this monoculture system. I'm going to start over, the right way this time; I'm going to set up a diversified organic farm in South Dakota near the Black Hills. I traveled through that area years ago and it reminded me of this country, but with a longer growing season. I'm going to build Tom's living legacy, a farm that works with nature and all that is beautiful in this world and doesn't wage war on insects or children."

"But why do you have to move for that, David? Think about Tessa. Here I can care for her, and for you and Jody. How are you going to manage all by yourself?" I argued.

And even though the words I spoke were true, the source of my protest was my fear of losing my son and his family all over again. How often was I going to see them if they moved to South Dakota?

"Mom, I don't have all the answers. But I know we have to move. I have to be able to see beyond Tom's shadow, to work towards a future that will be better for other children, and for Tessa. I understand how hard this must be for you and Dad, but I cannot do this here."

I'm sure he could read the disappointment on my face when I didn't respond. What could I say? My son had gone through hell and back, and had found a new purpose for his life. How could I argue with that or try to talk him out of it? My husband and I would simply have to make an effort to make the drive down south for a visit as often as possible.

"I haven't thought about the details yet," David broke the silence in an effort to explain himself. "I don't even know the first thing about how to grow an organic diversified farm. I only know it's what I have to do. I want to make an active contribution to make this world a better place. It's the least I can do in remembrance of Tom."

And so in the fall of 1996 David put the farm up for sale and went for a few weeks to the Black Hills in South Dakota in search of a new piece of land; new soil to root a new dream and a new foundation for his family.

KRISTEN SMITH, ENVIRONMENTALIST.

I hadn't heard from David since the day I left Maple Creek. One morning the phone rang.

"Hi Kristen, it's David, David Green from Maple Creek. Remember me, we met at..."

"Of course I remember you, David. Great to hear from you. How are you?" I answered, and observed how the warm feelings in my belly welled right up after being dormant for over two years.

"Oh, it's a long story. Do you have time for coffee? I'm in Hill City."

"Hill City, South Dakota? You're here in the Black Hills!?" I interrupted, dumbfounded while my heart picked up its beat. "What are you doing here?"

My voice danced with joy.

"All part of that long story," he said without responding to my enthusiasm.

I could sense he didn't want to share more over the phone. Something was weighing on his soul. I couldn't resist the thought that he might have left his wife. Guilt flooded my conscience when this caused my heart to pick up another beat. For a split second I felt like Cinderella and imagined my prince had arrived in search of me. Then, I quickly banished that thought. David sounded too somber for that.

"A bit further down the street from this payphone is a bar and grill, the Bumpin Buffalo. It's an old brick building with a lot of western charm. I was planning to check that out tonight. Do you want to meet me there for dinner, say at seven?" he continued. "I'm tenting at a nearby campground."

I had blocked off my evening to get through stuff I had to do for an environmental campaign I was organizing. Yet I heard myself say, "Sure, I'll meet you there. You've got a good eye; the Bumpin Buffalo is one of my favorite spots to eat in the Hills.

"It's so incredible that you're here. I can't wait to see you tonight."

I couldn't concentrate anymore that day. I must have checked the clock every ten minutes; the time just couldn't pass quickly enough.

The bar was just over an hour's drive from my home in Spearfish. Two hours before our meeting I was making myself pretty. Not that I was ever a girl for a lot of make-up, but that night I wanted to look my best.

Excited, I walked in the Bumpin Buffalo a few minutes before seven and eagerly scouted the historic western bar and grill for David.

"Here, Kristen!"

David was sitting at a table along the red brick wall under the painting of a majestic buffalo. A faint smile graced his gentle face, but the dark bags under his eyes betrayed the tiredness of a man who had journeyed through an agonizing darkness. Like the real gentleman he always was, he stood up and helped me to sit down. He forced some small talk, told me how good I looked, asked about my day and how long it took me to drive out there. We ordered some juicy buffalo burgers and fries, then ate in awkward silence. There were hardly any customers in the place. It was late October and the tourist season was over. In a week the bar would close for the winter.

I could sense David was trying to find a way to start his story and I was too nervous to prompt him.

He finished his burger, took a sip from his beer, looked at me with broken eyes and stammered, "Tom died."

Tears shot to his eyes as he spoke the words.

"Oh, David, I'm so sorry."

I took his cramped-up hand into mine and gently stroked it.

He paused, swallowed his emotions and told me the entire story.

He also told me about a little boy, Raul. Then he reached inside his breast pocket and took out two pictures.

"Now I carry the pictures of two innocent boys close to my heart," he said. "I'm not going to make it three."

I could see how his lip trembled. He could barely keep himself together. I didn't say anything. I only squeezed his hand.

When he collected himself, he continued, "I've seen how our food is being produced, both in North America and in a developing country like El Salvador. I've had a chance to get to know the economic slaves of this world; the people whose lives are disposable; the people whose liberty is framed between the choice of death or economic slavery; the people who are trapped in this system and will never be able to pursue their dreams; the people who are shot, assisted by our weapons and military, if they dare to stand up for their rights, if they dare to stand up to pursue their happiness.

"I've tried to comply with this system and paid for the betrayal of my conscience with the life of my son. It's time to do something, to make a difference!"

I felt his sorrow, his anger, his guilt and his resolve. David was going to carry his cross and make sure it counted for something.

"I don't have a real plan," he said, "but I do know that the world we've created is doomed. We don't care about our fellow human beings; we accept that others, people with dreams and aspirations just like you and me, live in the most horrific circumstances working six or seven days a week for twelve to fourteen hours a day so they can provide us with cheap food, clothing, electronics—just about everything. At the same time, we are all on the payroll of these corporations, some fictional entities that only exist on paper. And without thought, in their names, we execute strategies that rip this planet apart, pollute our air, poison our water and destroy our soil. And all for what? So that the corporations can make money; some paper prints that can be used to trade? So that our country can boast about some GDP growth, another set of meaningless digits? Have we forgotten that we cannot eat, drink or breathe money?

"I cannot comprehend why we all keep running on this treadmill without seeing what's happening to our world, without thinking about the future of our children, without at least attempting to take action, even if it's one small step towards a different world; a world in which our children can live in community; a world in which they can live in harmony with the earth; a world of abundance, joy and peace."

He paused. The world around us had collapsed to this little cocoon that sheltered us both. A woman, still in love, quietly listening, holding the hand of a heartbroken man who, for the first time in a year, poured his heart out.

David didn't look at me. His eyes were fixed to an obscure spot on the table, but his gaze pierced right through it into the depths of space and time. He searched for answers, a path, some direction, but found none.

Suddenly his eyes locked onto me; they had changed, were cold as ice. "Maybe the revolutionaries in El Salvador were right. Maybe it's time to grab a gun and shoot some of the corporate bastards who think they can hide in their ivory towers, drinking champagne and eating caviar bought with the dollars gained from selling poison that kills little boys."

I felt a chill go up my spine. What had happened to the gentle caring man who told me years ago that violence wasn't a solution? That day in the center of the Black Hills, I learned how hardship can change a man; how suffering can transform the soul.

"I know you're hurt, David, and I'm so sorry for what happened. But I'm not sure that shooting some executives will lead to change. Think about it; the corporation will still exist, and those men will soon be replaced by others.

"Think about the violence in El Salvador; did it change anything? Did it make life better?"

Our roles from a few years ago were reversed. At that time, I was the one who wanted to fight, although for me it was more something to say than something I really considered. But somehow, I sensed that the man in front of me could snap and would be capable of such savage action.

David was silent, his eyes aimlessly wandering through time again. For a moment his shoulders deflated in defeat. But then his posture recovered.

"I cannot comprehend why we don't act and change this society." He paused, pondering the thought, then continued,

"Truthfully, I don't know what to do myself. I don't understand the system; I don't understand the mechanism that herds us onto the treadmill and keeps us there.

"I first need to study this world, read what they teach in universities and more importantly, read what they don't teach the students of today's world. I do know this world cannot change if we all keep creating the same reality we see displayed around us every day."

"You have to consider, David, we didn't get here overnight, and just as well it's going to take time to reverse the tide and free us from the grind," I said, relieved to see a sparkle of hope return to his eyes. "If each day more people accept their accountability and start to make conscious choices towards co-creating a sustainable world, then some day, together, we will reach that reality," I added, fueling this more constructive approach.

"Well, I've enough on my plate anyway," he said, finding his old self again. "I'm here to buy some land. I'm going to start over, build a new farm somewhere in this area, a farm that doesn't fight nature but works with it. I'm going to grow an organic diversified farm here in South Dakota. I can't stay back home; there is too much that reminds me of Tom. And these hills here remind me of the Cypress Hills at home. I was hoping you could help me find a place."

"That's great news!" I said, overjoyed with the prospect of seeing more of David.

He shared how the past year had been, told me about Jody's depression and Tessa's need for some motherly love. Then he confided his anxiety about his vision for a new farm. "I feel like I'm in kindergarten again," he said. "I don't know the first thing about organic farming. Well, I guess I do remember some of the things my father did when I was a kid when he still had a traditional diversified farm. But there's so much I have to learn."

"You should go to Cuba," I told him.

"To Cuba?" he questioned, surprise in his voice.

"Yes. Cuba had a highly industrialized agricultural system until the start of this decade when political circumstances forced the country under threat of starvation to change its ways. Now, seven years later, they are on the leading edge with regard to sustainable farming practices."

I could see a glimmer of curiosity and adventure taking root in David's eyes. The young man who set out to travel across North America with the field pickers and who ended up volunteering in an orphanage in El Salvador with his newly-found wife-to-be was still hiding in there.

But I also realized the man in front of me had changed. Life had left some permanent scars on his soul. I still loved him though, and wondered what role I could play in this new chapter in his life. Could I help him to enjoy life's beauty and nurture his sensitive nature?

"I know of a university professor up in Canada who organizes farmer exchange programs between Canada and Cuba," I said encouragingly.

The discoverer's curiosity faded, and instead a glimpse of harsh determination flickered in his eyes again. "Sounds good. I'll go to Cuba to learn about organic farming," he said. "And while I develop my farm, I'll study and learn to understand how this system can be changed. Once I find a weak spot, I'll strike it. This world has to change, for the sake of humanity, all species and this planet."

I hoped the hardness that flashed through his eyes would soften with time, and with new love.

I know it did, even though most people wouldn't understand.

I have kept the testimonials from all the people I talked to as authentic as possible and revealed their names, age and relationship to my father. What follows though is one exception. It is of an organic farmer from South Dakota, a friend of my father, a man with the same zeal for healthy food and sustainable farming. He only agreed to include his testimony upon condition of anonymity; he was fearful of retributions from powerful seed and food corporations.

As will become clear from his story, this man's fear was based in reality. So I have respected his wish not to reveal his name. The omission, however, doesn't make his testimony any less true or significant.

ANONYMOUS, ORGANIC FARMER.

I met David for the first time in the summer of 1997. I was selling vegetables at the Rapid City farmers' market. He came just as the market was about to close. "Another bargain hunter," I thought at first. In truth though, we love all shoppers who visit the market— those who come early, and those who come late in search of a bargain. In the end, none of us farmers want to take any of our vegetables home. The purpose of the market is to arrive with a full truck and drive home with an empty one. Veggies just don't keep well till the next market.

That day, I was almost sold out, and there were still some twenty minutes to go so I wasn't in the mood to drop my prices just yet. He bought some tomatoes and to my surprise didn't ask for a deal.

"I noticed all your produce is organic," he said. "My name is David. I just bought some land north of the Black Hills, close to Bear Butte. I had a farm up in Saskatchewan, Canada, and moved to this area last month. I want to get into organic farming here and would appreciate some advice from a local. Would you have time for coffee or a beer?"

I didn't live in the area. South Dakota is a big state, and all land is different. My farm was close to Chamberlain, about three hours east of the Black Hills close to the Missouri river. But the community of organic growers is small. Any time another farmer considers taking the plunge and sets out on that fulfilling but challenging road, I'm prepared to make a little contribution of time if that helps them on their way.

So I agreed to meet with David after the market. I was confident about selling out and hadn't planned anything for the afternoon. It was the start of an unexpected friendship that lasted for years.

During our first meeting David was kind of formal—going through his list of questions about what to grow, where to sell, potential wholesale distribution of organic produce, the most common pests and diseases that affected crops, and so on. He sure was thorough! When we didn't manage to work through all his questions, we arranged for another meeting the following week after the market, provided I would sell out again. That summer having coffee with David became a regular item on my agenda following the Black Hills farmers' market.

Even though David told me he had never farmed organically, I could quickly tell he wasn't a novice. Of course he was a farmer, and he had already done quite a bit of homework on growing organic produce.

But when I asked him where he got schooled on sustainable farming practices, I received a most unexpected answer.

"Cuba!" he announced.

He must have noticed the surprise on my face.

"I had the same reaction when a friend suggested that I visit Cuba to learn from their sustainable farming skills. I joined a Canadian/Cuban farmers' exchange program last winter," he explained. "Cuba is fast becoming a leader in the world with regard to organic farming."

Cuba was not much talked about in the U.S. However, I had heard rumors about how their health care system rivaled that of our country at only a fraction of the cost. Their doctors made a whole lot less, and focused on preventative health care. What a concept!

"I guess they were forced to farm organically due to the trade embargo we forced upon them in the 60's," I replied.

"Well, yes and no," David explained. "The embargo at first redirected Cuba's agriculture towards the Soviet Union. And instead of being a major provider of tomatoes and fruit for the American market, they became the prime provider of sugar, rum, cigars and tropical fruits for the Russians. In those years they practiced monoculture farming, just like any other country infected by the green revolution. They sprayed tons of synthetic fertilizers and pesticides to produce their crops, and they fed their animals huge volumes of grain. At that time they had one of the highest tractors-to-acre ratios in the world.

"It was the collapse of the Soviet Union in 1989 that created the turning point for Cuba. Overnight, their export market collapsed, and they didn't have any means to import the machinery, chemicals or grains on which the conventional agricultural model is based."

"Well, if they were able to create a state of sustainable health at a budget, I guess it's not too far of a leap to see how trade shortages can focus a country's agriculture on feeding its people through sustainable farming," I pondered, impressed.

"They went through hell though to get to that point," David continued. "Overnight the country went from a standard of living that was just as high as in America to a state of poverty. In one year Cuba lost about sixty percent of its food supply, and was struggling to feed its people. An adult's daily calorie intake dropped from three thousand to nineteen hundred within months! That was low enough to be at risk of starvation. The Cubans now refer to that period as the 'special period.'

"When I traveled to Cuba I stood on the edge of blemish-free fields of organic potatoes, beans and cabbages that reached as far as the eye could see. In the past, organic farming always brought pictures to my mind about diehard hippies and old-time stubborn farmers who work small plots of land only to prove a point, but unable to make a real living or raise a family, let alone feed a population. But the farms and co-ops we visited were sophisticated operations, often thousands of acres in size. They had exchanged chemicals for green manure, crop rotations, earthworms, composting, pest- and disease-monitoring, biological control programs, waste recycling, and bio-fertilizers and free-living bacteria that provide nitrogen for crops. What struck me most was the combination of these scientific and effective bio-methods applied at such scale with only oxen and workers in the field."

"They work thousands of acres with oxen?" I queried. To this day I remember how awestruck I was by this.

"Yes, and their yields are back to levels similar to those before the 'special period,' and in some cases they're higher. Their circumstances forced them to focus on food. They're now even producing food on rooftops and balconies in their cities. Havana alone produces forty-five tons of vegetables annually in such a manner. I visited one such city garden; they're called *organoponicas.* For this particular one they had ten people producing enough food for four thousand city folk."

I was speechless. In truth, I wasn't quite sure if David was serious or taking me for a ride.

David was quiet for a while now, staring into the distance like he was replaying memories only he could see.

"I'll never forget Pedro," he said. "Pedro and his fellow farmers helped me to remember why I chose to become a farmer years ago. It was something I had forgotten over time as I tried to keep my head above water and distanced myself from the land in ever bigger machinery with ever bigger engines and wheels to cover ever more land in less time. But when I joined Pedro in the field and worked alongside him for a day, I not only saw the twinkle of humble pride in his eyes, but I shared it; the pride of a healthy crop and soil; the satisfaction of a hard day of labor; and the gratitude for the wonders of life and nature. It was something I had forgotten. Pedro gave me that spark of life back."

This time I knew what David was talking about. It was a connection with the land I was lucky enough not ever to have lost, or at least not for long.

During our meetings I had questioned several times what had motivated David to sell his seemingly successful farm in Canada and start from scratch here in South Dakota. He had shared with me everything he had learned in Cuba, but never what had brought him to travel to Cuba and caused his sudden passion for organic farming.

After one of the September markets that year we took off to Custer Park. It was the week before the great buffalo roundup. Our meetings had become more extensive, and instead of just having a beer or coffee somewhere, we had taken to the hills on some hikes. We didn't talk too much that day. I think David had pretty much shared everything he had learned in Cuba, and I had provided all the advice I could about organic farming in South Dakota.

Without us opening up about our personal lives, our conversation wasn't going to go much further. I had already told him about my wife and my three boys who all helped out on the farm. I had even invited him over for a visit. But besides a mention of a friend who lived in the Black Hills, David hadn't shared any of his personal story.

After a few hours hike, we sat down in the tall, straw-colored grass on top of a knoll overlooking a large herd of buffalo grazing down in the valley along the creek. David must have sensed how I wanted to ask him again about his family but didn't because I had learned to respect another man's privacy.

"My son died from leukemia almost two years ago now," he said while gazing out into the distance. Then he told me his entire story and invited me over to meet his family at his new farm.

That day, I became a family friend. David was truly a remarkable man. Life had dealt him wounds that would take many men down, but not David; he had readjusted, learned from his mistakes and was determined to make up for faltering. David was going to leave a legacy in the name of his son. "I'll start with providing food for people without harming this earth," he said. "Who knows where else that will lead?"

KRISTEN SMITH, ENVIRONMENTALIST.

I wish those years of David's Black Hills farm had never ended. David initially bought two sections of land with an old weathered homestead just north of Sturgis. The soft rolling lands dotted with patches of Colorado pine were covered with native grasses and were home to a herd of buffalo.

"Why would I keep cows here? The animals don't plow through the snow to find food in winter, and they cause a lot of sleepless nights during calving," David explained. "Buffalo were made for this country; they know how to survive and to calve on their own, and their system changes for winter so that they are more economical for a farmer to keep than cows during those cold months. On top of that, buffalo meat is healthier, leaner and tastier."

Some of David's cultivated fields curved with the terrain and were taken through a crop rotation program year after year. David grew beans, peas, squash, pumpkins, carrots, potatoes, tomatoes, oats, rye and hay.

In the distance Bear Butte rose up towards the sky. Bear Butte is one of the most sacred sites for the Lakota and other tribes and is recognized as the geographical center of North America—or, as it is called by the natives, Turtle Islands. David had baptized his family's new home, "Crazy Horse Fields."

"Crazy Horse roamed these lands," David explained. "He was a brave Sioux warrior who kept fighting to the end to protect the harmonious way of life of his people. He refused to settle and accept the ways of the white men. I'll need some of his spirit to defy the conventional farming methods and join those who lead the change towards a way of agriculture that is in harmony with these lands."

When I first saw the farm and the homestead, I couldn't imagine what David would make from it over the years. The house must have been from the turn of the century, and was more or less falling apart. There wasn't a lick of paint on the siding anymore. But in its own way, the grey barn-board look created a charm that spoke of a hidden and unknown history. The once-cultivated fields around it were overgrown with weeds, and the pastures' fencing consisted of worn grey rotten posts with orange-rusted wire that, at long stretches, ran in curls over the ground instead of stretching along the fence-posts.

David invited me over a few times during the first month they moved in. I think he enjoyed some other female contact other than Jody's, given her depressed state. I accepted the opportunity with open arms and soon visited on an almost weekly basis.

Slowly but surely I saw the lush organic farm rise from the rubble. After some quick tender loving care to make his new home wind- and rain-free, David focused his attention on his fencing and pastures, and quickly had a buffalo herd which he rotated through several connected grazing lands.

During his first winter he started to improve the house. His first step was to renovate Tessa's bedroom. He painted the walls girly pink and purple, and restored the old plank wooden floor.

"Got to make sure my princess feels at home here," he said.

Tessa's room looked out east over the rolling hills and Bear Butte. One time when I stayed for the night at Crazy Horse Fields, I fell asleep in the rocking chair while comforting Tessa during a thunderstorm. I woke up in the early morning when golden rays of the light entered the room, and I witnessed the sun climb into the sky from behind Bear Butte. Those majestic sunrises must have infused David's daughter with the positive energy she came to possess.

Besides Tessa's room, that first winter he fixed up the kitchen, guest room and living room. I assisted with much of the painting, and added a female touch to the decoration so that in the end the home embraced the family with warm yellow, red and orange earthen colors.

David only got to renovate the master bedroom during his second winter at Crazy Horse Fields. Maybe for Jody's benefit, David should have positioned their bedroom to capture that powerful energy of the rising sun instead of the western setting sun. You see, Jody still spent most of her days in bed or listless on the couch. Only the odd time you would see her play with Tessa. When that happened, it was something Tessa talked about for weeks.

Due to the frequency of my visits Tessa soon called me "Auntie Kristen." I was more or less her big sister—for which I was too old—and her surrogate mother, for which I was too young. So "Auntie" it was. It fulfilled me to be able to give the young girl the love she was missing from her mother.

Not that Tessa would ever show that she was missing anything from Jody. She'd come home from school, run to her and embrace her without ever showing the slightest sign of concern when her mother only returned that embrace in an act of unemotional auto-response instead of offering a warm welcoming hug, smile or kiss. Seemingly oblivious to Jody's depressed state, Tessa would tell her with a voice full of excitement every detail of her day at school.

Children are such examples of unconditional love. In even the direst of circumstances they still don't question the love of their parents. It's simply something they accept as a fact. It was Tessa's way to care for her mother; to bless her with the love she had to give in the hope of helping her heal. And at times, a flicker of joy appeared in Jody's eyes and a soft smile formed on her face. But almost as soon as these moments appeared, they faded into the darkness of past pain and guilt. It was like Jody wouldn't allow herself to embrace life again in Tom's absence, like she felt some kind of guilt at the first spark of joy or happiness.

I helped Jody as best as I could to take care of her family. I helped with the cooking, did the laundry and the dishes, cleaned the house and attended Tessa's basketball games. At first I tried to chat with Jody, but I soon gave up on that and accepted the silence that filled the kitchen when we were cooking together. I usually made enough meals during the weekend so they only had to warm things up on weekdays. On good days, Jody came to help. I told her which vegetables to cut, and she would do that. But if I hadn't been there, David would have had to do all the cooking himself. After a while, just like Tessa, I would tell Jody all about my past week without ever expecting any response.

Most of my weekends and vacation days I spent at Crazy Horse Fields. Whenever I had to skip a weekend due to an environmental campaign or other work-related matters, I would miss the family and feel guilty that I wasn't able to care for them that week.

And while I told myself how much Tessa needed me, how important it was to help this family, in truth I spent my time there because I was in love with David.

My favorite moments were the summer evenings on the porch after I put Tessa to bed and David helped Jody settle in their room. We would sit together on the large swing bench which he'd built from the wood of an old fallen Colorado pine, and watch the sunset while leaning against each other. Or in winter we would sit in front of the crackling fire in the living room, snuggled together, soaking in the warmth of the touch of our bodies. I would share with him the environmental projects I was working on; we would discuss the campaigns I organized, analyze how the world got to this point and brainstorm about solutions for sustainability. He would share how his latest thinking had evolved and the ideas, discoveries and myths he had come across in the books he was reading.

At times he would lie down on the couch with his head in my lap and I would run my fingers through his hair while we conversed till deep in the night.

I'm sure he enjoyed that bodily contact as much as I did. I even think it aroused him just like it made my body ache for him.

I remember how more than once, he would enter the kitchen and stand behind me, putting a fleeting hand on my hip while looking over my shoulder into the pots on the stove. I could smell his scent and feel the warmth of his strong body behind me while the air of his breath stroked my neck. Those moments were so erotic that I could have made love with him right there and then.

Anyone seeing us during those years would have thought we were man and wife. It actually even felt like it, with one exception—we weren't sharing the same bed.

Even though David was open to some physical contact—he even sought it out at times—there was also a clear invisible line that he wouldn't cross, a boundary that was sacred and one he wasn't planning to violate. At least not just yet. I took solace in what I did get from our strange love relationship, and hoped the day would come when that boundary would be crossed, or better, be erased.

ANONYMOUS, ORGANIC FARMER.

David and I became good friends over the years, even though we lived some three hours apart. We had a lot in common. Just like him, I hadn't always been into organic farming.

I had studied agriculture at college and had been more or less brainwashed on the need for the green revolution and factory farming in order to increase yields, bring food costs down and feed the world. I was taught how the use of the modern hybrid seeds combined with the right amount of synthetic fertilizer produced premium yields over the farming methods of old. This was largely due to the invention of pesticides which allowed us to control and secure the health and safety of large monoculture crops. It was only later that I discovered independent research that demonstrated how organic farming methods could produce similar yields and were more resistant to drought and other adverse weather conditions, making them a more secure way of farming.

My father died early in a farm accident, and when I inherited the farm in my mid-twenties, I started to pour on the synthetic fertilizers, set up a monoculture operation and entered the game of chasing higher yields and expanding farmlands in a market of rising costs and decreasing prices. I was still single at the time.

The following year I met my wife. When I proudly showed her the farm for the first time, she said, "I don't see how you can be a Christian and put poison on food."

That's when things changed for me. In truth, I was more concerned with losing my girl than with figuring out how the chemicals fit into my faith, but I thought she had a point. So I invited her to help me return to the diversified ways of farming my family had always practiced and make sure we would be able to make a living that way. I think that's what eventually led to our marriage and kept us together for all these years. The day she asked that question we became a team. She helps with the farming—and probably does more research on it than I do—and I help with the cooking. It's the flip side of the coin; after you grow the food, you still have to prepare it.

It gives me a certain pride and deep satisfaction when I can cook a meal with all homegrown ingredients—peas, carrots and potatoes from the garden; a piece of hormone-free longhorn beef from a cow that was pasture-raised at my farm; some milk from our goats.

My life wasn't burdened with the perils David went through, and I never took the time to live out the adventurous cravings which I think every young man has. And so I enjoyed listening to David's stories of his past.

In just a few years David's farm was thriving. We were both vendors at many of the same farmers' markets, and allocated sections of our land for crops to sell at these venues. Just like me, David would find organic processors who were prepared to lock in at a premium before he planted anything. Why put a crop in the ground if you don't have anyone who wants to buy it?

I know it's quite different from how most farmers work, but think about it; which other businessman would invest in something without a solid sales projection? The way government rules work today, it has turned farming more into a gambling business with a large social security net so you can never lose.

Most guys put in one or two commodity crops, and then have to accept whatever price the corporate-controlled elevator offers. Through farm subsidies and disaster payments the government encourages the growth of crops that were meant for the deep rich soils of the Ohio River Valley, on marginal lands where disasters aren't freak incidents but a normal, almost annual, occurrence! Farmers receive direct payments each year when the commodity prices fall under certain levels, no matter what they grow or how they grow it. The large corporations that control the grain processors, cattle feeders, seed companies and meat processors all profit from overproduction since that drives the commodity prices down, while taxpayers' money ends up feeding corporate profits and keeping most farmers afloat from one crop to the next.

On a regular basis I would take my family to visit Crazy Horse Fields, and David and his family would come and visit us at my farm just east of the Missouri river. We would walk each other's fields and discuss the health of the soil, some of the new things we'd tried and pest- and disease-control methods.

But it was the dinners that I will always remember, and which I miss the most. David had such a large library, and was always reading new books about sustainable agriculture, social systems, our economy, democracy, and human rights and values. To David all those things were interconnected. He firmly believed that the way a society connected with its food was fundamental for the respect and values within that society.

When our families met though, it was kind of strange since David always showed up with two women—Jody, his wife, and Kristen, the family friend. When we first visited his farm, I thought it was more of a coincidence that Kristen was there. Over the years, though, I came to understand that Kristen almost lived there. When David's family would visit us, Kristen would be with them. He once explained to me how lucky he was having Kristen there to help with the household due to Jody's depression. And when you saw them together, you couldn't quite figure out which of the two was his wife. David would take such tender care of Jody, and then chat with Kristen like they had been married for years.

I know of course that Jody was David's wife and that he was faithful to her; David was a man of his word. But my wife told me she thought more was going on between Kristen and David. She said she saw it when their eyes met. I guess it's something that women notice. In any case, I told her to stay out of it. It wasn't any of our business, and David, Jody and Kristen seemed quite happy and had found a good balance despite Jody's state of mind.

At the dinner table Jody never said much, although I'm convinced she enjoyed the conversations since she never retreated to her room as long as we were there. Given the distance between our farms, my family would often stay overnight and return home early the next morning.

We spent Thanksgiving of 2001 at Crazy Horse Farms. David's parents also visited from Canada. On special occasions like that, we sometimes did a little gift exchange. Nothing big, often something we had made ourselves or a nice antique gardening or farming tool we had picked up at some auction. That year, I had taken an old piece of barn-wood and burned in some words from Franklin D. Roosevelt: "A nation that destroys its soils destroys itself." It was my gift for David, and functioned as the topic of conversation that weekend.

"Roosevelt was right," said David, "but it's the same as saying the glass is half empty. At times it's important to understand the graveness of the situation, but in every tragedy there is also an opportunity. When we discover the lens that sees the glass as half full, we find new strength in the power of hope. It's when we realize we always make a difference, no matter what, that we find our true power."

"Guess you don't like it all that much," I said in reference to my gift.

"Oh, I do. Thank you for this. I'm going to hang it on my office door. I didn't know Roosevelt occupied himself with the quality of the soil. It's encouraging that men like him had such wisdom. And every time I walk into my office I'll remember what I'm working on—a nation that builds its soils saves itself, and a nation that nurtures its soils creates itself."

I now have a piece of barn-board above my garden with that inscription on it signed by David. He gave it to me on Thanksgiving the following year.

"It's about time we get a president who's as smart as Roosevelt and as insightful as you are," I said. "Someone who starts using those farm subsidies in a way that rewards farmers for the service they deliver to the nation and for the way they grow their crops rather than strictly for quantity and overproduction."

"That's what they do in some European countries," Kristen said.

Kristen could always tell us about the latest scientific research or sustainable practice in just about any part of the world.

"In Denmark and Sweden, farmers receive government support for transitioning to organic and sustainable farming methods," she continued. "On top of that they're paid ongoing support fees for the protection of wildlife corridors and the elimination of toxic runoffs that pollute the groundwater and waterways."

"Now that's using money of the people for the people," David said. "It wouldn't work here since the corporations wouldn't make a buck on it. In North America we use the money from the people for the benefit of illusive corporations that poison our children."

David would be like that during those years. One minute he would inspire us, see how he could make a difference and focus on the creation of a better world. The next minute his anger would surface, and he would lash out against those who got rich while being complicit in the death of his son.

"You're right," I had to agree. "The proof is in the pudding. With all those farm subsidies over the last thirty years, the number of farmers is still dwindling and the industrial farms are gobbling up the land and becoming ever bigger and meaner. If the government would apply that money effectively, it would help to build our communities instead of destroying them."

"And there're now a large number of independent studies that have uprooted the myth that chemical farming produces higher yields than organic low-input farming," Kristen said. "Sustainable farming yields are, in the short term, mostly the same and outperform conventional farming yields in the long run because of their healthier soil which retains more water, organic matter and nitrogen. On top of that, organically farmed soils function as a carbon sink and contain over twenty percent more carbon than industrially farmed land. It not only keeps all of our families healthier—producing food that tastes better with a higher nutrient value—but it also helps to combat global warming."

"Amen," I confirmed. I could see Kristen was all excited now. Frankly, it was a joy for me to see her get passionately swept away in her argument.

"We've been told for years about the economies of scale and how industrial farming is required to feed the world, but guess what?" she asked, her eyes twinkling. "I recently came across another conclusive study that proves that smaller farms have a higher dollar output per acre than large farms, one that's often up to ten times higher! The conventional paradigm is just another myth to justify the concentration of land holdings into the hands of the few for the financial benefit of the few."

David changed the tone to a more positive trend. "What gives me hope, though, is the rising demand for organic and quality food," he said. "That gives me hope."

"As with all change in history, it's going to have to come from the people," Kristen concluded.

That winter David bought another section of land just east of Bear Butte. I had advised him to stay away from the major biotech crops like Canola, corn and soybeans. But I guess David wanted to prove something. He had grown Canola in Canada using the chemical farming methods, and now he wanted to prove that he could grow just as good a Canola crop using organic methods.

TIM BENNETT, FRIEND, BUSINESSMAN.

It was the spring of 2002 when I ran into David again. I attended an executive retreat in the quaint town of Deadwood, located at the center of the Black Hills. I'd never heard of the place before, and certainly didn't expect to see David in this heritage mining town.

My company had rented the historic Bullock hotel, which transported arriving guests to a time-long-gone of gunslingers, gamblers and outlaws. After check-in I wanted to take a stroll downtown, to time travel to an age when men on the frontier were in the chaotic process of building this great nation. I walked out of the hotel and literally bumped into my old friend David. We hadn't seen each other for over two decades—since our summer trip after high school.

"Excuse me," I said and wanted to get on my way, but I had this flash of recognition. I guess it was his eyes, still shining with a vitality most other men didn't have, although now they seemed scarred by some unknown pain and guilt. David was heavier and stronger, but still fit and well recognizable.

"David?" I questioned.

David looked at me with an almost hostile, piercing gaze. I remembered his dislike of men in suits when we were teenagers, and figured that hadn't changed. And here I was, on top of my game, in a tailor-cut suit, partly balding and with quite a bit of extra weight on me from all the business dinners and social functions which my position required me to attend. But then he recognized me, and a broad smile wiped away his initial reserved look and his eyes flickered with excitement.

"Tim? Tim, is that you?"

The smile on my face gave away my answer.

"Wow, it's so great to see you!"

He opened his strong arms and took me in a warm, uninhibited embrace.

"What brings you to Deadwood? You're the last person I would have expected to see here."

"Well, I guess I could say the same," I said.

"Do you have time for a beer?" he asked.

"Sure, I was just going to check out the town. I love the historic character. Not sure though why they picked an old town that was home to miners, gamblers and outlaws for a banking retreat."

"Oh, that's easy enough. They're all thieves!" David blurted out. When he saw the irritated look on my face, he glanced over my suit and I could see how he realized his clumsy insult.

"I'm sorry, Tim. I didn't realize. You must be a banker."

He smiled to relieve the tension. "As you can tell, my views haven't changed all that much over the years," David said calmly with friendliness in his voice. "I won't hold it against you. I'll make it up to you; I'm buying the beer."

We walked into Saloon No.10 in which Wild Bill Hickock and Calamity Jane used to hang out, and where Wild Bill was shot and came to his end while playing poker. The long wooden bar, the golden brown wooden walls and ceiling covered with old paintings and pictures, the antlers and mounted deer all spoke to the imagination of a life on the frontier.

"Boy, it's been a long time," David started after we sat down and ordered two beers.

"It sure has," I agreed.

"Remember that morning when we reached the ocean in White Rock?" David said, nostalgia in his eyes as his gaze drifted off to the images of a youth that had slipped through our fingers.

I only nodded, joining him on the journey through our memories.

"I'm so glad to see you again," David said returning to the present. "How have you been? How was university? Has life treated you well?"

I gave him a snapshot rundown of my life. I had studied economics, and passed my Masters in Business Administration with honors. I had met my wife at university, and we settled in Toronto where I got a job at the head office of one of Canada's biggest banks. Slowly over the years I worked myself up the corporate ladder and now was responsible for a significant portfolio of international financial loans and investments. My wife and I were blessed with two children, a girl and a boy. Last year the company relocated us to New York to be closer to Wall Street, the heart of the global financial world.

David listened. I would impress most people with my career story—but not David. Even though his face didn't betray any sign of judgment, I knew he didn't approve. What bugged me was that I cared. Why did I care what a man whom I hadn't seen in over two decades thought about me and the choices I had made in my life? I know he had been my best friend while growing up, but we had gone our separate ways. It was already clear in high school that we would grow apart. I changed the subject; it was time to focus the spotlight on his life.

"So what have you been up to, and what brings you here?" I asked.

He took a deep breath and sighed. "It's a long story."

"Well, I have time, and I want to hear it," I encouraged him.

And so David told me about his travel adventures, a little boy, Raul, whom he had left behind in El Salvador, his marriage to Jody, their two children, Tom and Tessa, and the farm they had built in Canada.

"So what brings you here?" I interrupted him. "Are you guys on vacation in the Black Hills?"

"No, I live here now," he said. "I have an organic farm just north of Sturgis."

"Was it the warm weather or all the bikers that visit Sturgis for their annual pilgrimage that brought you here?" I asked, smiling.

"Tom died when he was twelve," the harsh, broken reply came. "It was cancer. I killed him with the chemicals that were sold to me by one of the largest corporations in the world, Empuro. It's run by men in suits who claim their products are safe to spray on crops and then make a ton of money from farmers like me who don't know any better."

His tone had hardened, and the friendliness had faded. It was like we were teenagers all over again, having the same debate we had years ago. This time though, we had the experience and the battle-scars to back up our positions.

"I'm very sorry to hear that, David," I emphasized. "But surely you can't blame yourself for this. There are so many different things that cause cancer. You can't jump to the conclusion that spraying pesticides killed your son. If there had been a real danger in spraying, there would have been government regulations against using the products."

I should have left it at that, and maybe he would have understood that I was merely concerned about him and how he took the blame. But I couldn't resist continuing.

"I can tell you're angry with the executives of the chemical company that sold you your pesticides, but I've been dealing with people at senior management levels of such corporations and I can assure you they are nice guys. They're guys just like you and me with dreams and aspirations and a lot of drive to make them happen. None of them sit in their office wondering what to do next to harm people. On the contrary, they provide the products and services that help this world to deal with the challenges we face."

"I'm sure that's true," David said. "They'll sell you anything for money. It's all about money!"

"What's wrong with money?" I asked, a little agitated. After all, money was my life.

"Everything and nothing!" he answered with a sigh as the harshness cleared from his voice. He looked me in the eyes, and I could see his despair. But when he continued I realized his desperation wasn't rooted in his suffering, but rather in his struggle to help others see the world through a different lens, his lens.

"I didn't go to university, Tim. Life has been my teacher, and life has taught me we live in a screwed-up world. Imagine a helpless nine-year-old boy whose parents were taken away by soldiers in front of his eyes, imagine him looking in your eyes when grave danger faces him, and imagine walking away from him because some stupid imaginary border restricts your rights in helping a fellow human being, an innocent child in need of help and love!"

"I understand you faced some tough things in your life, David, but you can't blame it all on money or people who have money."

"Every day, with every act that supports the current system, we're putting a child somewhere in the world into such dire circumstances. And when challenged, we turn our backs as long as it doesn't happen to our child. But someday, Tim, it might be your child, or your grandchild. Trust me, I turned my back! I tried to comply, to fit in with the way agriculture is going, and look at the price I paid. No parent should pay for the enrichment of an elite few with the life of their child—not here in our developed world, and not in any developing country on the planet."

I could only agree with that, but still thought David's views were distorted due to the suffering he had endured.

"I agree there're some evil people in the world and many tragic things occur," I said, "but because I have money, does that make me evil, does that mere fact turn me into a heartless bastard or a killer? I do care about people and this planet, David, and I try to use my skills, knowledge and wealth to help make things better."

David looked at me with eyes full of compassion, but still with that trace of desperation. For a minute he was lost for words. Then he said, "Tim, I know you're a good man. You always had a good heart. That's why you're my friend. Even though we haven't seen each other for years and might not again for a long time after today, you will always be my friend. Anyone can see the honesty in your soul."

His words made me feel warm and appreciated, and I remembered again why I had always enjoyed David's friendship. We could disagree, have different views about the world and passionately debate them, but David's friendship was never conditional upon agreement; it was based on values of integrity and respect. David was a man of the heart.

He continued and said, "There's nothing wrong with the concept of money, Tim. But money does have the power to make good people do bad things. Sometimes people know they're contributing to something bad, but most often they don't."

"Give me an example," I challenged.

"There's many to choose from, but here is a recent one that's currently in court and has been called one of the largest environmental disasters in America. There was a company in a small mountain town in Montana that mined vermiculite until the early nineties. The vermiculite was contaminated with the worst form of asbestos, and there is strong evidence that the company's executives knew about the contamination when they bought the mine in the sixties. More than twelve hundred people died of asbestosis, a form of cancer caused by the asbestos pollution. A class action lawsuit has now been launched.

"Turns out the same company poisoned the water wells of people in another small town in Massachusetts, which led several people to die from leukemia. Both of these places are now superfund sites.

"In Montana the mine declared bankruptcy, but the company itself restructured and today is still making billions of dollars in sales. So what I don't get, Tim, is how such companies can survive such scandals, and how the executives of such companies manage to stay in power?"

David had hit on a side of business none of us want to talk about. So I tried to deflect the question.

"But that's one out of a sea of companies, David."

"As I said, there're plenty of cases to choose from. You surely must have heard the case of one of our big American car companies that led to the worst auto crash fire defect in history. Over eighteen hundred people burned to death in their trucks because of a known design defect that was caused when management ignored the advice of their engineers in order to create an added key-selling point. When the company was asked to recall the vehicles, they refused. When some managers suggested changes, they were turned down. And why? Because according to the company's cost-benefit analysis, it was cheaper to pay the legal charges to the accident victims than to spend two dollars and twenty cents per car to change the design.

"Since Tom's death, I've been reading a lot, Tim. I needed to know if the death of my boy was an isolated incident. I needed to know how we could allow corporations to do such things. I still don't understand why our governments allow such things to happen and how the executives of such corporations can take such actions in good conscience and manage to sleep at night. But it's clear from the long list of tort cases and class action lawsuits against corporations that executives act first for the financial benefit of their corporation, without considerations of conscience or regard for life itself. There are even cases where American corporations, in cooperation with the CIA, have been linked to the overthrow of governments in developing countries to protect their financial interests. What makes matters worse is that they are financially well-rewarded for such deeds."

I wasn't quite sure how to respond. These were the stories that poisoned capitalism and made us all look like bad guys. I couldn't deny what David put forth, but also knew that most companies, and most men, weren't like that.

"Tim, I've experienced the price to be paid for the pursuit of wealth by men in suits in faraway board rooms both in El Salvador and in my own family. What causes people to act like that? How can they do this without being punished? If you know, please tell me."

David's eyes flared up with the same passion for justice I had seen years ago during the model United Nations conference, but this time it was rooted in real pain and his pleading came from true desperation.

"David, you have to put this in perspective. You have to consider the good aspects of corporations as well. Think about the comfort and wealth that has been created by this same system," I said. "Think about the house you live in, and imagine if it didn't have a furnace and gas piped to it, or any of the materials that are now widely available to provide you comfort in your home. Think about the television that provides for your news and entertainment, the flight you can take to travel to Mexico for a vacation, the phone that allows you to stay in touch with your mother and father up in Canada, or the clothing that keeps you warm in winter. Imagine life without all those things the current-day corporations and economies provide. In order to make an accurate balance sheet, you have to look at both sides of the equation.

"And all those companies that make money from providing these things people need and want, they give back to their communities by sponsoring the environmental and social problems of this world through the NGOs that focus on those."

I waited for David's response, thinking I had made a convincing argument to bring balance to the situation he had presented.

But David replied without hesitation, "Tim, all those comforts you talk about, I'd give them all back in a heartbeat if I could get my son back. I'd give them all back if I could save little Raul in El Salvador from the horrors of civil war. What kind of person is prepared to offer the life of children as a price for comfort?"

The strength of my presentation evaporated in an instant. How could I argue with a man who had paid such a price?

Then David continued to shoot down the second part of my argument: "I realize that corporations today are major sponsors of charities and other non-profit organizations, and you say that makes them good corporate citizens. But would you pardon the SS in Nazi Germany for what they did if they had sponsored a food program through a charity to help undernourished children in concentration camps? Or would you pardon a killer for finding foster care and a school for the children of the parents he killed?"

"David, that's an unreasonable comparison, and you know it!" I protested.

"Is it, Tim? Aren't all those financial contributions to charities and the talk about 'corporate social responsibility' a simple and effective distraction so that people stop asking questions about the true cost this world pays for the enrichment of many large companies' shareholders and executives?"

I wasn't quite sure how to continue the conversation, and wanted to change the subject to something much lighter, away from this part of business that I didn't want to examine, when David said, "But let's go back to my original question, Tim; what is it that makes executives act in such a manner? Sure these people have a conscience, so why do they leave it at home when they act on behalf of their company? Isn't there such a thing as business *ethics?*"

"The corporate charter demands that executives act in the best short-term financial interest of the company's shareholders," I responded. "It's the law. And if an executive puts his conscience before the financial interest of the shareholders, he violates the law and can be sued."

"You're saying the *law* demands that leaders of corporations act without a conscience? These men often have more power and wealth than entire countries, and you're telling me that our laws don't allow them to act with a conscience?! Go figure!"

"Well, the idea behind capitalism is that society works best if it's left up to each man to pursue his own financial interest. The government's responsibility then is to regulate and police the rules of the game, and as long as any corporation and its executives adhere to the government's rules, they can follow their primary purpose—to make money," I explained.

"And what if they violate the rules?" David questioned.

"Well, then, they pay a fine."

"Seems that isn't doing much, since it only leads to them calculating the cost of the fine versus the potential profit that they can make by violating the rules," David scoffed.

"You know what happens, Tim, when people drive too fast, or drink and drive, and then kill someone in an accident. They have to pay huge fines, a serious sum of money to the victim's family, and it's very likely they'll go to jail. But what happens to corporate executives? Tell me, who went to jail for poisoning the well water of those people in Massachusetts, or who went to jail for making the decision to design trucks with gas tanks that explode upon impact? *Who went to jail for killing my son, Tim?"*

How could I respond to such a question? I couldn't even maintain contact with David's piercing eyes, which were attacking the business tribe to which I now belonged.

I knew executives rarely went to jail for such things, most often because they had the protection of the most powerful legal firms money could buy. And even though the legal framework still existed for revoking corporate charters should a corporation cause mortal harm, hardly anyone knew about this, and it was generally not seen as a viable legal strategy. Some corporations had even become so powerful that they were now seen as too big to fail, for the financial and social impact of that failure was by most politicians and media channels regarded as too large of a price for society to pay.

"I've seen and experienced the fallout of a world absorbed with making money," he said. "At first I watched and did nothing, and then I turned my back; I didn't want to face the truth, and instead tried to comply. I paid with two lives, one of them that of my own son. But I did receive something in return, Tim."

The strength that had come into David's voice here surprised me in light of the tragedy he was talking about.

"I have a purpose now," he continued. "Everything I do is focused on making a difference in this world. My organic farm makes a difference on a micro scale. And some day, when I understand the underlying faults in our current society, I'll attempt to create a macro change that benefits our children both here and in poor countries.

"What's your purpose, Tim? What's the purpose of a banker? What's the legacy you'll leave behind when you die? Will the numbers in the bank accounts mean anything?"

The questions that David left me with that day haunted me for years.

KRISTEN SMITH, ENVIRONMENTALIST.

The unexpected meeting with his school friend, Tim, made a significant impact on David. During the months that followed he burned through book after book. His focus had shifted significantly from sustainable living and farming to economics and politics.

One summer evening we went to a barn party following the wedding of the daughter of one of David's neighbors. Over the years people had gotten used to seeing us together; most knew about Jody's depression, and had heard Tessa call me, 'Auntie.' We might have been the subject of gossip to some, but the majority of the community minded their own business and had accepted that David was often accompanied by two women.

Jody didn't enjoy celebrations or parties. Over the years David had encouraged her to attend in the hope that such events would allow her to embrace the joy of life again, but he hadn't been successful. Finally, at one point, he came to the conclusion that Jody's pain would stay with her to the end of her days, and he stopped trying to brighten her existence. He continued to be kind and loving to her—that never changed—but he came to accept that the cheerful lively woman he had married was gone forever. And so whenever he was invited to a social event, he would ask me to accompany him instead. Jody didn't seem to mind.

At the wedding party, friends, family and neighbors all had gathered together to celebrate the love of two people and the commitment they had made to walk through life together.

The evening started with the savory smell of sizzling steaks on the barbeque. Fresh garden salad, tomatoes, beans, potato salad and corn finished off the meal. For dessert there were slices of watermelon, cantaloupe and chocolate cake. As we mingled, David and I caught up with neighbors and friends on the crops they were growing, the impact of the dry weather, any new animals that had been added to their farms, and of course the growth of their children—their success stories, and the common challenges of their age.

The men decided to get together for harvesting and wood chopping, and the women were planning some canning and jam-making bees. This was country living and community at its best.

After dinner we were invited to the barn's loft, where a makeshift bar had been set up and a band played some great country tunes. David and I danced our hearts out.

David was a passionate dancer. He told me that before Tom's death he and Jody couldn't keep their feet still when they heard a tune, and they would always steal the show on just about any dance floor.

"You're a true blessing," he said with a smile on his face after we had been swinging for a while. "I had forgotten how much dancing makes me feel alive. It's so liberating to abandon life's movements to the rhythm of the music."

Seeing him so happy and knowing that I had made him feel that way made me all fuzzy inside. I so loved this man. When were we going to consummate that love?

The evening ended with the parents of the bride playing a few songs for the newlyweds. The mother strummed the guitar while the father picked the banjo. It was truly endearing, and the radiating friendly and grateful energy from those who witnessed this celebration was proof of how the love that lived within this family had touched everyone's soul.

The night was warm, the moon waxing and the crickets chirping as David and I walked home, hand in hand, to Crazy Horse Fields.

"What an inspiring evening," I said. "My feet are killing me from rocking all night, but my heart is still dancing. I feel so alive at this moment. There's no way I'm going to be able to fall asleep any time soon."

"Tonight was a display of human strength; love and camaraderie at its best," David said.

While I had observed how the evening had impacted my soul, David had focused on the larger social picture. I wanted him to forget about the world for a moment and focus on our relationship; on the connection and joy of our souls.

"We could have a family like that," I said softly.

"We have a family like that," he answered without hesitation, and put his arm around my shoulders. As always he knew how to walk this fine balance by tenderly comforting me without crossing a line. And as always he would make sure I knew where that line was.

As David spoke again a determined vibration in the tone of his voice suggested we should remain on the topic of conversation he was setting. I knew he didn't want to talk about us.

"It's amazing how all over the world people can gather and share their joyfulness through laughter, conversation and dance, on occasions that celebrate life and love. I once attended a funeral held by an Irish family, and they had just as much fun as they danced to honor and celebrate the life of the deceased, the life that once had been."

I suppressed my urge to talk about our relationship. I didn't want to ruin this near-perfect evening, and so I listened, curious as to where David was taking this.

"When someone witnesses the celebration of a new birth, a wedding or anniversary, or even a harvest or farming feast, it's impossible not to be touched by the joyfulness of the experience. It's like those miracles of creation connect at a deeper level and make our soul dance, despite any of the day-to-day challenges we might face.

"Did you know there were farmers present tonight who were at risk of losing their crop? There was even one family that might lose their farm. Yet they showed no sign of the challenges they're facing. And just like everyone else they danced and laughed, infected by the blooming love between a young man and a young woman."

We walked on in silence, and I wondered when our love would infect people like that.

"So how have we come to create a world that revolves around money?" he said, breaking the quiet imagery of my thoughts. "Have you ever seen such joy and enchantment when people reach a certain financial goal? They might be happy, even throw a party, if they become millionaires, but it won't infect everyone that visits in such a way as it does when we celebrate love and life.

"And if love and life are what we celebrate, then why aren't they the driving force behind everything we do in our society?"

As always David asked questions no one else did.

"I don't understand how we got here, but I do know why things aren't changing," he continued. "People are so caught up in trying to keep their heads above water that they don't have the time to question the foundation of the system that governs their lives. And as soon as they have a break, they either rest or find a reason to celebrate life and love so they can find new inspiration to step into the rat race again.

"And on those few occasions when they do try to understand what makes their life so challenging in this society, they're only able to analyze it from within the system because of their brainwashed state. And so they find more creative ways to play the monopoly game and improve themselves based on its rules. This means that whatever they do, it will always benefit the system that makes the rich richer and the poor poorer.

"Nothing in the world changes because hardly anyone takes the time to question the rules of the game, or the game itself. Should we be playing monopoly? Or should we invent a new basis for our society; a driving force with rules inspired by life and love, benefiting all people and creatures on this planet? How long can it last, this selfish, meaningless, monopoly game we currently play? Where does it lead to? How does it support our values of democracy, freedom, equality and brotherhood?"

Silence accompanied us for the rest of the walk home, even though I'm sure David's mind was all but silent. "Wait here," he said when we arrived at the porch.

He went inside and soon returned with two picture frames. He took two pictures from his breast pocket, framed them and hung them above the door. "The love of these two little boys has inspired this farm; this is what has grown from their lives and deaths. They should look over it, and their faces should touch everyone walking through this door. Crazy Horse Fields is a celebration of their love."

Before we entered the house David said, "I have to find a way to stop this corporate theft. Tonight I witnessed and felt how the human spirit is still alive. I experienced community and the values that count in life. It's worth saving. These boys died to inspire the dream of a better world, and I've seen its power tonight. It's worth fighting for."

But a better world for me also included expressing the love I had felt deep in my bones that night. It was a love worth fighting for.

When I visited the following week, David asked: "When you joined the protest in Seattle against the WTO, what did it feel like?"

"It felt like we were finally doing something," I answered. "It felt like enough people were standing up to create a real change. But we'll need more people to join this movement and get up from behind their television and get on the streets."

"Isn't there another WTO meeting coming up in Mexico?" he asked.

"Yes, this fall in Cancun. It's in September, and I'll be going," I said.

"I'm coming with you. I want to know what it feels like to stand up together against this system," he said.

For the first time we would travel together—to Mexico! The emotions would be raw there, the feelings heartfelt as people rallied together against the mighty and powerful.

Barriers between people come down during such events, as they connect on a deeper level. If there ever was a time for the boundary between David and me to come down, this would be it.

LETTER FROM DAVID TO JODY.

Thursday, September 11th, 2003.

Dear Love,

I'm sitting here in the dark on the beach near Cancun writing you under the silver light of the full moon. The soft sound of the never-ending breaking waves reminds me that time moves on, but also that the patterns of history repeat themselves in never-ending cycles, each of them similar but different; unique in its own way just like any wave that reaches this beach. The events today were dramatic. It's the middle of the night, and most protestors and delegates are asleep. But I couldn't wipe the images from my mind and kept thinking about our time in El Salvador. So I decided to find my way to the beach, wander for a while with my feet in the ocean, trying to understand the feelings that rage inside of me.

I miss you! I miss you so much. I miss sharing experiences with you, and your strength and guidance in times like this.

Given the dark and early morning hour, I guess the events happened technically yesterday—September tenth—but for me they still belong to today.

Today was the march of the peasants, the *campesinos*, as you recall they are called in Latin America. I was excited since this was my first protest march. Imagine it—me, who never believed in protests. Yesterday already there were activist actions, but Kristen and I had chosen not to participate. Instead we wanted to connect with this place and this land. We did that in a unique way, and went swimming with the dolphins. It was absolutely amazing. I wish you could have been here to join us for this.

Dolphins have a healing power. They touch your soul and make your spirit dance as it connects with the splendor of creation. Their skin is soft as silk, and you can feel their love while they tenderly touch your feet before they push you powerfully forward like a surfer carves through water. There's something that's beyond comprehension about the connection I had with these creatures of the sea and how they sensed and responded to my respect, love and gratitude. I have some pictures which I'll bring home for you.

Yesterday was a day of discovering the magnificence of creation. Today was a shock into reality of how harsh the fight to protect God's wonder really is; how desperate the situation is, and how real the price is—the price paid to allow a minority in the world to control all the wealth and power, and the price that will have to be paid to take it back.

The day started in a festive mood in Casa de la Cultura, the eco-village where the *campesinos* camp. We joined a group of American and Canadian farmers who have come to support the peasants here in their cause to demand food sovereignty—the right for countries to produce their own food—and the ban on patenting any seed—life itself.

While farmers from across the world—although mainly from Mexico and Central America—were gathering around the food tents this morning, a giant drum circle formed. Activist college and university students had arrived from their camping place at the stadium. They were dancing guided by the drumbeat while indigenous grandmothers dressed in colorful woven shawls approved of what they saw with broad smiles. The energy was alive and vibrant. Here were people, thousands of people, joining together, celebrating the common values that connect us to this earth while honoring our cultural differences.

We marched from the barrios to the wealthy hotel strip of Cancun in the company of two colossal puppets representing Kukulcan, the feathered-serpent God, and Chac, the Mayan God of rain.

Contingents of *campesinos* marched behind their banners, the women in traditional dress, the men identifiable by their unique scarves. I felt an urge to march up front, and joined the *campesino* group from El Salvador as the Americans were asked to march further back. There was something very satisfying in joining together in the fight with the people I had once abandoned. This time, I was shoulder to shoulder walking with them ready to face any of the police violence that could come our way. Kristen had prepared my battle dress; two water bottles, a bandanna and goggles as protection against pepper spray and gas. The crowd chanted their songs, beat their drums and clapped their hands along the way. There were thousands of us, ordinary citizens, and punks dressed in black with masks who called themselves the "Black Block." We marched side by side with poor peasants. It was an imposing display of the power of a people, a people joined together by the oppression of corporate greed.

The march came to a halt at the junction that gives access to the hotel strip, which looked more like Miami Beach than the Latin culture of Mexico. A large fountain with Mayan pillars in the center marked the junction. The way ahead to the conference complex was blocked by a steel barricade with police in riot gear behind it. For a moment the front lines stopped to observe the enemy. Then both Latin and Korean peasants challenged the fence. The Koreans had a coffin with them, which they burned, declaring that the WTO killed farmers. Then, in an act that defies imagination, one of the Koreans climbed the fence and plunged a knife in his own chest.

I rushed forward, and in the midst of Korean men who reach as high as my shoulders, caught the collapsing man as he fell down. Together with his fellow Korean peasants we laid him on the pavement in front of the barricade. Blood gushed from his chest and dripped from his mouth; gurgling sounds from his breaths betrayed his pain, but his lips graced a faint peaceful and satisfying smile. As the medics rushed through, the God of rain, Chac, seemed to approve, and blessed the offering of life with a heavy downpour. The rain was cool and invigorating, and the masses welcomed the refreshment with arms raised in the air on this hot and burning day. Most had seemingly missed the tragedy that had just played out, and the battle went on with punks and *campesinos* attempting to tear down the barrier in a combined effort.

But I couldn't erase the image from my mind, and the desperation of a man who killed himself to give power to the cry of the peasant movement and their critical predicament across the world.

The fight intensified. A Black Block brother climbed the fence and a policeman crashed a baton down on his head. More blood flowed, even though the brother didn't seem to be hurt too badly. A giant American flag was burned—my flag; a flag of liberty and a flag I should be proud of, but a flag under which today's people from around the world are trampled in the name of democracy and freedom, and a flag that has been taken hostage by corporate power and now works to advance an agenda of money and greed.

The police put on gas masks, the masses were throwing stones, and I still couldn't shake the image of the Korean peasant who offered his life in battle, a battle beyond the interest of his family, beyond the boundaries of his country, and beyond farming communities across the world. It was a battle for the right to food, water and shelter; a battle for democracy, life, liberty and the pursuit of happiness.

Then I picked up a rock, and with all my rage and pain, slung it towards the policemen defending men in suits who were legalizing the plundering of this world. The crowd was enraged, more rocks were flying, and the energy was boiling. And just when it looked like things would get out of hand, a surreal scene developed. A juggler stepped into the space between the ever more threatening police force and the crowd. Rocks were flying all around him as he started to toss his clubs. And like a true magician he wove a calming spell over the crowd with his magic performance of catching dancing clubs from the air in a silent hypnotic rhythm. Students edged us back, and we started to chant: *"El pueblo unido, jamas sera vencido!* A people united, will never be defeated!" As our voices reached a crescendo the tension ebbed and the crowd pulled back.

Some gathered in the shade and started making speeches, but Kristen and I chose to walk back to the encampment. At first there was nothing to say; the killing scene just kept repeating itself in my mind. I wanted to know who this man was, what was his story, what had led him to this selfless act that empowered the voices of the voiceless. Word spread quickly through the camp, and by the evening I knew the man was referred to as "Lee," for his full name was too foreign for many to remember or pronounce. He was a farmer, a leader of his community, a married man, and the former president of the Korean Advanced Farmer Association. He had staged a hunger strike at the WTO headquarters earlier in the year where he had declared, "Reaching to my conclusion now here in Geneva, at the front gate of the WTO, I am crying out the words to you that have been boiling for so long a time in my body. For whom do you negotiate now? For the people or for yourselves?"

An activist from India told me Lee's death had made the suicides of hundreds of thousands of peasants visible. When she saw the look of disbelief on my face she said, "Each year over two hundred thousand farmers are committing suicide because they have been pushed into debt by mighty global companies. There's a massive corporate genocide taking place—the killing of people for super profits—and no one is telling the story because the media is owned by those who profit from this slaughter. That's why Lee killed himself in such a public way. He represents the hundreds of thousands of voiceless farmers who went before him."

Ever since we left El Salvador I had shied away from keeping up-to-date with the fate of peasants and other oppressed people in the developing countries of the world. It wasn't very difficult to do since we would rarely find out about the fates of these people on the evening news. While I had struggled with the challenges farmers in North America wrestle with every day, the events of today and the realization of the scale of global oppression that is taking place crushed the significance of my own problems.

Kristen and I joined the wake for Lee tonight at the Casa de la Cultura where people from different cultures from around the world honored our fallen brother. The *campesinos* had created an altar decorated with flowers, candles and pictures of Lee which they had decorated in the form of a cross. Traditional Mayan prayers and Christian prayers were offered, and the Korean delegation bowed to the altar in a Buddhist salute. Lee's death had not only given voice to the injustices that were happening to farmers, but had also broken down any differences in cultures and religions as all could feel the power, sincerity and sacredness of each prayer.

As I sit here on the beach my mind drifts back to the revolution in El Salvador, the resistance of the rich and powerful to share their land and wealth with the people of the country, the failure of the peaceful attempts for change by the Church, the assassination of Monsignor Romero and, in the end, the spreading of the violence of the revolution.

And I wonder, in a world where laws are passed by men of power and wealth, in a world where those laws are enforced by the legalized guns of men of power and wealth, in a world where sovereignty capitulates to the rules of men of power and wealth, and in a world where people are blinded by myths and lies spread via a media controlled by men of power and wealth, in such a world is there room to grow something new; something based on love, diversity, gratitude and respect; something that can live in harmony with earth; something that brings joy and peace; and something that nurtures our children and allows us to die knowing we did well for all the generations to come?

Or is the sacrifice of life, the storm of destruction and pain; an inevitable step in opening space for something new to grow? What will it take for us to create something better for our children; something that recognizes the right of all people and creatures to freedom, equality and the pursuit of their dreams?

Love,

David

SOARING EAGLE, LAKOTA ELDER.

The Creator weaves people's paths together for a reason. And so he did with the lives of David and me.

It all started the day following Lee's death during the WTO protests in Cancun. I joined an evening protest march towards Ground Zero; that's how we referred to the place where Lee died. The crowd was beating on pots and pans, and several people were carrying torches. Like a snake we moved through the city expelling the spirits of evil with fire and drumming.

At Ground Zero, the Koreans had set up a memorial for Lee, an altar with flowers and candles. Different groups had offered banners in tribute to Lee's life and sacrifice. As we arrived the Koreans faced us holding white candles. We honored Lee in powerful silence, fists raised, a bright moon overhead. There was respect, strength and defiance in the air. We, the people, were prepared to sacrifice to rid the world of the evil system that has us in a chokehold.

Then someone shouted: "Lee!"

And the crowd answered: *"Presente!"*

"Allende!"

"Presente!"

"Zapata!"

"Presente!"

"Romero!"

"Presente!"

The roll call of the dead went on for a while. When it stopped the man next to me added: "Tom. *Presente!* Raul. *Presente!*"

He was wearing a T-shirt with a print of the Crazy Horse memorial on it. He was white, tall and muscular. I first took him for a tourist who had visited the controversial Crazy Horse Memorial in the Black Hills. White men often wear such T-shirts as a trophy of their travel achievements without knowing even the slightest bit of the values of the brave warrior.

But here we were marching side by side for the same cause, revolting against corporate power, so I became curious. The march continued; we circled the fountain, and then headed back. I was still walking next to the same man, so I asked: "Did you visit the Crazy Horse Memorial?"

"I did. Not sure though he would appreciate the mountain being carved up in his image. I don't think that's what he fought for."

I liked his answer. It seemed this man had at least made the effort of reading something about Crazy Horse.

"Where are you from?"

"The Black Hills, just north of Sturgis," he said and then continued. "I named my farm after him—Crazy Horse Fields. I work with the land there now, but these were your lands, the lands where Crazy Horse roamed. I try to respect it in the same way, and hope his spirit of courage, humbleness and leadership will infuse the path I've chosen to follow."

"Bold for a white guy," I thought. I was intrigued to find out more. David and I spent the evening together and became friends.

It's funny how the Creator works. David and I were practically neighbors.

"Funny how close we live," I said. "I'm from the Pine Ridge Reservation in South Dakota."

My home was only a few hours drive from David's farm. But we had to meet in a foreign country far away from home, fighting with people from across the globe for freedom, and our human rights, honoring death and in doing so cherishing the value of life. Truth is, if I had run into David for the first time in South Dakota, I probably wouldn't have had any interest in starting a conversation with him. I would have thought him to be either a tourist or a redneck, and neither understands the deep connection my people have with our land.

"Who are Tom and Raul?" I asked.

He looked at me with suspicion.

"I heard you call their names when the death roll came to an end," I explained.

"Tom is my son," he said, "and Raul came to me as a son." Then he shared his life story while we made our way back to camp.

This white man had been tried by life and was determined to make a difference. He had also learned from the land and seemed prepared to make the necessary sacrifices. He didn't have his head full with illusions of a world of loving people waving candles in one global peace movement. I considered taking him with me to the circle I was attending later that night.

Turned out that the woman David was with was attending another meeting at the Convergence Center that evening.

"So what's life like at the reserve?" David questioned when finishing his story.

"It's like trying to recover from a torture experience," I replied.

"I'm not sure I understand."

So I explained, "Years ago I read an article about a CIA torture manual that was discovered. It spelled out the psychology of torture, and the inhumane techniques of using sensory deprivation and intermittent sensory overload like electroshock and other ways of inducing intense pain as a way of breaking down the victim's sense of self. The goal was to wipe away a human being's self-respect and personality and bring the person to a child-like state so that the tortured man or woman would start to see the interrogator as a father figure.

"What happened to our culture is similar. The North American Indians, just like most indigenous people all over the world, have been brutally shocked into regression, a regression of our culture. The way of life of my people has been entirely destroyed, and with that our identity as a people.

"What the torture manual doesn't teach is how you rebuild an identity after it has been destroyed. The reason is obvious: torturers are not concerned with the fate of their victims. And so it seems that the white man is not concerned with the fate of the Indians, or any other people they destroy in their imperialistic drive for wealth and power. That's why there're no road maps for developing a new culture and identity. The only solution the white man saw was integration. But integration was only a further extension of their torture and destruction."

David was listening. I knew that his experience in El Salvador allowed him to understand what I was talking about without becoming defensive of his race. He knew I was only sharing my history in answer to his question and that we know there are people of the heart among all races and cultures.

"So what does all that mean for day-to-day life at the reserve?" David asked again.

"The Pine Ridge is the poorest place in North America, yet we're surrounded by the richest country in the world. The average life expectancy for men is forty-seven; for women, fifty-two. Eighty to eighty-five percent of my people are unemployed, and about half of them live below the poverty level. Some twenty percent of our houses have no plumbing or telephones, and as tiny as they are they provide shelter for an average of seventeen people. The infant mortality rate for our children is five times as high as the national American average, and our youth is four times as likely to commit suicide to flee this living hell.

"Most Americans don't even know about our existence! The only time you hear about an Indian on the news is when one of us gets drunk, steals something, or kills someone, but never do you hear about our brave warriors who work diligently day in, day out, to help our people rise from the rubble and build a new and proud Lakota society."

"Seems similar to what happened to black people in America," David observed.

"Worse," I said. "Blacks were slaves, but that also meant they had an economic value. We Indians were only a nuisance, as we were free men. We defended the freedom of Mother Earth and all brothers and sisters that live on Her, so we were of no value since the white men's society is based on property rights—in essence, the right to exclude others. They can't show our current suffering on the news since it reminds them about the genocide that took place on Turtle Island and on which America is built.

"You should come and visit one day," I offered. "I'll show you around; take you to Wounded Knee, where the cavalry murdered three hundred peaceful men, women and children after the Americans broke their peace treaty that created the Great Sioux Reservation and presented us with seven smaller unconnected reserves, all to get to their illusive gold, which was discovered in the Black Hills, the most sacred ground for my people."

"I'll take you up on that offer," David said, and I could see the sincerity in this man's eyes.

The Creator had brought us together when we were both bringing honor to the highest sacrifice of all—life—on the eve of an important circle, a circle to start a new world.

"I'm meeting tonight with other indigenous elders and *campesino* leaders from around the world," I said. "Would you like to join us?"

"I'd love to," David said.

"You might not get a lot of sleep," I warned. "The meeting isn't taking place here. We'll have to travel for a couple of hours."

We met with my contact Armando, a Mexican *campesino* leader who had fought with the Zapatistas, and with Pablo, a Peruvian Shaman. For two hours we drove through the darkness into the depths of the Yucatan rainforest. When we got off the highway, we drove through a small village, then onto a back road, further into the jungle.

As soon as we stopped, Armando urged us to follow him. We walked close behind him so we wouldn't lose sight of him. The forest was dark, with the only light some silver streaks of the moon that peeked through the thick tree canopy. The sounds of the jungle were leading us from the harsh fight in Cancun into a world of magic—a different dimension of the universe.

The forest opened up and we passed through a large open plain, on which an ancient pyramid sat, bathed in the silver light of the moon.

"Chich'en Itza," Armando said as he walked steadfastly past the large pyramid. "This is sacred land for my people."

I noticed glimmering flashes of light further in the jungle and could hear voices. Armando led us to a round stone platform. Some leaders and elders had already taken their place in the circle.

The platform was surrounded by eight torches, two on each side of a single stair leading up to it from each of the four directions. A short distance to the west was a larger pyramid, similar to the one we had passed in the open field. At the same distance to the east a smaller pyramid rose up from the jungle floor. Torches burned on top of both pyramids, throwing amber light on the Mayan shamans who were seated in prayer at the center of the pyramids. I could feel the presence of the ancestors and the power of the many circles that had taken place here.

"Americans always think the big pyramid is the most important one," Armando said. "It's because they interpret things from within their cultural perspective where bigger is better. Where we are praying and meeting today though is the world of people, for the bigger pyramids represent the realm of the Gods. As above, so below."

David was quiet, taking everything in with the eyes of an explorer. We took a seat in the circle and engaged in the normal welcoming conversations, introducing names as well as the place we came from and the people we belonged to. People kept arriving from different directions of the forest, and soon twenty of us were seated around the fire in the center of the circle.

One of the Mayan shamans took the lead and offered corn, coca leaves and tobacco. I offered to pass the pipe around which I had brought. Once the opening ceremonies were completed, the Mayan shaman spoke.

"We've come together here tonight under the guidance of the female powers of the moon to stimulate the free-flowing of ideas. We are seated on top of the only circular platform on these sacred grounds of our ancestors. The circle represents all that is, all that has been and all that will be. It is the eternal and the now; it is the all-encompassing and the singular point of oneness. This is the universe and the center of the universe. This is everything that encompasses life, and the center of it where everything is born from and returns to. The temple to the east represents Venus, and the temple to the west is Osario, the High Priest or masculine power of the world. Medicine men are praying on both of those temples to help us harmonize the duality of this existence. We will end our gathering on top of the great pyramid when the sun rises in the morning, and the masculine energy of the universe will add its power and determination to our vision. Tonight we will recreate the world."

The medicine man sat down and silence engulfed the circle while each one of us contemplated the profound importance of this meeting. A tribal leader from Colombia was the first to speak.

"My name is Danilo. My people are the Arhuaco. We live in the Sierra Nevada de Santa Marta. Our priests have kept this world in balance throughout the ages. The Sierra is the center and the heart of the Great Mother. But today the ice is melting on top of the mountains and our people are being killed at the foot of the Sierra at the hand of cruel soldiers. Mother Earth is in pain and at risk. We are a peaceful people, but unless our younger, immature brothers wake up from their ignorance and see the power of the Mother, we will face devastating consequences."

The stillness of the circle allowed us to absorb what had been said. Then the next person spoke.

"My name is Mutang. My people are the Petan, and we've been called the last of the nomadic people in Southeast Asia. We live in the Borneo rainforest along the Batam river. But we are nomadic no more.

"Some thirty years ago, most of our people lived in the forest of Borneo. From the forests we received our life. It nurtured us and provided for us. It was our home and our kin. Everything in the forest has a name and has meaning to us. The forest lives, we are only a part of it. Some of our elders visited cities in countries to the north, and we couldn't believe the tales of poverty they returned with. We learned about people who were starving and banned from the community; they were called 'homeless.' This is a grave violation, which we call *sihum*—the failure to share. It's a breach of the core values that represent the wealth and strength of a community.

"The home of my people was demolished over the last couple decades as the sounds of over a thousand bulldozers replaced the morning howls of the gibbons and converted over a million acres of rainforest into dead timber at a rate of eighteen million cubic meters per year. This past year the last of our people settled in poverty in the dirty shacks the government offered us after they took our home, the jungle.

"Government officials told us they bring us development. But we see only dusty logging roads and the destruction of our home. We don't understand how this so-called progress is good for us when it only brings dependence, the loss of our culture, starvation and the demoralization of our people. Government officials tell us they will make things better and create jobs for us, but why do we need jobs? My father and grandfather never had to rely on anyone to create jobs for them. Our language has no term for employment or unemployment. We lived from the land and forests, and it was a good life. We were never hungry. The forest provided well for us. The forests have sustained our people for thousands of years, but the jobs they offer us logging this forest will be gone when the trees are gone. What will become of our people when the forest is gone? It's time to stop this attack on our home, Mother Earth, no matter what!"

One by one all members of the circle spoke. Men and women from all corners of the globe gave testimony to the annihilation of their people and the destruction of Mother Earth, all for the sake of what was called "progress." I spoke of the history and predicament of my people. David spoke of his journey and the losses along the way.

"The time has come for us to act," the Mayan shaman said. "We have to be the living prayers. We are nearing the beginning of a new cycle, a new world."

"We have to stand up and fight," a Zapatista peasant said.

"You'll have no chance," a white woman from Wales said.

"We should follow the path of peaceful resistance," someone else said.

The debate and the difference in views as to how to change the world went on for hours.

Then David spoke up, "Trying to fight the destruction sounds to me like trying to fight a forest fire. We all know that the forest fire will end when the forest has been burned. So can we find a source of inspiration in the destruction, can we find inspiration for growing a new forest, can we find inspiration for that which will replace what once was, can we find inspiration for the new society we want to grow?"

The distant roar of a jaguar added power to David's words.

"But what if life itself is threatened?" a younger Incan man from the Andes challenged. "What if the fire eats the last tree, what if the biological pollution they cause now infects the last seed? How can we grow a new forest, a new society, without any healthy seed?"

"I'm not saying we shouldn't protect what's left," David said. "I'm only saying that we should know what we're fighting for. Fighting for a memory of a world that once was is not a vision that will mobilize a people."

The dynamic of the conversation changed, and my respect increased for this man whom I hardly knew. People started to talk about their common values and foundations for a new world. I heard words like diversity, respect, love, sacredness of life, equality, freedom, brotherhood and so on. Agreement started to form on the importance of connecting people closer to their food again.

"When a people's relationship to the food that nourishes them is lost, the respect for food and for our living environment that provides for such food disappears," a man from Brazil said.

"It was one of the things that struck me in Cuba when I participated in a Cuban/Canadian farmers exchange program," David said. "Farmers are some of the most respected people in the country. They are paid more than lawyers and bankers because they provide the population with its most essential service: food! One evening after

the Cuban farmers had thrown a barbeque and roasted a pig for the
visiting Canadian farmers, some of the shyness and reservation
disappeared, and as the rum flowed the conversation became more
open.

"We explored the differences between how farmers were
treated in a country as poor as Cuba in comparison with a country as
rich as Canada. And while the actual dollar numbers of the income of
Canadian farmers is much higher, the respect for farmers in Cuba and
the security they enjoy is something that can only be envied by farmers
of first world countries. When we explored what made the difference,
we concluded it was 'voice.' When ANAP, Cuba's forty-two-year-
old farmers' organization speaks, the government listens. Farmers in
Cuba are united.

"The people who are behind the 'takers' model of today's
world have played divide-and-conquer since the days of the Romans.
They've done it with farmers around the world by splitting them up in
commodity groups, regions or provinces. That's how the bureaucrats
play the game. They've done it with societies across the world, and
with all issues of social and environmental importance. It is by divide-
and-conquer that the corporations keep winning, for all of us are
fighting for connected issues in small, isolated groups. Our new
world should include a vision of being united in diversity."

I was glad I had invited David to this circle and had a feeling
he would take an important role in the work of this group. It was a
hunch that proved to be accurate.

By dusk the people were in agreement on forming a new
society under the name of the "Gaia Confederation." A lot of time
was spent on arguing over the terms "Pachamama" or "Gaia." Both
referred to Mother Earth, but each had a different cultural origin. In
the end it was decided to choose the term that would have the most

potential to connect with people in the developed world. It was felt that it was essential for the success of the new world that people in rich countries choose a new way of life that didn't depend on the exploitation of Earth, its creatures and other human beings in faraway countries.

When the sun rose above the horizon we greeted its first rays from the top of the first pyramid and presented the birth of the Gaia Confederation.

KRISTEN SMITH, ENVIRONMENTALIST.

I woke up in the morning, worried and lost. The space next to me in the tent was empty. On the night when Lee had taken his life, David had been restless, couldn't catch any sleep and ended up leaving the tent for a few hours, taking a stroll around Cancun towards the beach. But he was back by morning.

I'd come to love waking up next to him. I had enjoyed curling up in a spoon-like position, the back of my body pressed against him, his muscular arms around me in a protective embrace. Often I would wake up in the morning still in the same position. I would then lay still, afraid of waking David, and enjoy the sound of his breath beside my ear, the peaceful inflating and deflating of his chest as the life-giving air nourished his body.

When he woke up yesterday morning, I could feel he was aroused. I turned towards him. Our faces were so close that we were sharing each other's breath.

"Good morning, my love!" I said.

He only smiled back and gently stroked my cheek. I responded to his tenderness, and wrapped my arms and legs around him in an intense embrace while burying my face against the side of his neck. I could feel his muscles tighten as he held me, and I knew he wanted me. He kissed me on my forehead. Then his arms relaxed and he stroked my hair. We lay still for a while. I was anxiously waiting for him to cross the boundary, afraid of taking any further steps myself and ruining our perfect friendship. I knew he had committed himself in marriage. But no one could deny he loved me just as much. Why would God mind us expressing our love, setting it free, allowing it to dance in ecstasy? It was people and culture who had created those boundaries.

But I knew David was a man of his word. It was one of those things I admired him for. And so he broke the spell and said, "I think we should get up and find out what's on the program today." And with those words he assured my dream would stay just that—a dream, at least for now.

I did feel somewhat hurt and rejected, even though I had felt how much he desired me, and so for the rest of the day I kept to myself more than usual. So last night when the opportunity arose for each of us to get some space from one another and attend different meetings, I thought it was perfect and I could see how David welcomed the chance just as much. I had no concerns when I found an empty tent and fell asleep shortly after midnight. But when I woke up in the morning and realized he had not returned to the tent at all, I was worried in a way I had never been before.

Where was the man I loved, the man whose bed I had shared? He wouldn't be with another woman, not David. I for one knew how faithful he was. But knowing that only increased my sense of discomfort. I didn't know the native man he had left with, where they had gone or what had happened to him. What if he had been mugged somewhere; after all, this was Mexico, still a developing country with huge poverty. And those of us who are trying to make a difference in this world, who are trying to make things better for the poor in countries like this, don't have a sign on our forehead that reads "world savior." For the gangs of teenagers who learned to survive in the barrios, the sneakers we wear are of just as much value as those of a world-ignorant tourist.

I didn't know what to do. Should I report his absence? But what was I supposed to say, and to whom was I supposed to report it? I didn't feel like sitting for hours in a Mexican police office to report on the disappearance of a man who wasn't my husband. So I decided to get dressed, wash myself and get ready for the big protest march that morning.

The march scheduled for nine-thirty took off around eleven. Still there was no sign of David. I realized though how difficult it was going to be to find each other once I had left our tent, as some ten thousand people had gathered and were walking down the by-then familiar route to Ground Zero, chanting, drumming and singing. On the way the Mayan God Chac got stuck in a power line, and this was skillfully moved up with large sticks so that our now-beloved rain god puppet could bless us all.

Today was a women's day. We women would show the world that female power could not be caged when the world's children are expendable in the pursuit of corporate greed. When the peaceful and determined stream of people reached the fence at Ground Zero, I joined the women's contingent that was called forward. I looked around for David, but didn't see him anywhere.

With big bold cutters we broke through the chain-link fence that was attached to the orange steel barricade that had stood up against the pressure of the crowd for the last two days. Today we were going to take the fence down. The people would not be blocked out from the decisions that affected their everyday life! But I regretted David was missing this show of a people's power that had pervaded the masses.

From the other side of the fence nervous police in riot gear were watching us from behind their tall shields, batons in hand. We women cut multiple holes big enough for a person to pass through. The next phase was most perilous. Together with a number of other women I stepped through the fence and positioned myself between the police and the mass of people behind us. I was pressed against the riot shields, eye to eye with an ordinary man who makes a living following orders without fully understanding the issues at stake and the things we have in common. Our fight is as much their fight; they just don't know it.

"We're protesting peacefully," I said to the policeman who was only separated from me by the shield he carried. He didn't react to what I said, but rather seemed to look right through me.

"We won't apply any violence," I said in the hope of reaching the human soul inside of him and reducing my chances of injury.

The Koreans had braided long ropes, thick as a man's leg, and they were attaching them to the steel structure behind us. A woman a stone's throw away from me was hit on the head by a policeman who lost his cool. The tension was rising.

Adrenaline flowed through my body and heightened my senses. My heart pounded in my chest; my breath was shallow. Things could have gotten out of hand real fast—but they didn't. The ropes were attached, and we retreated back through the holes in the fence. People were lined up, the ropes in many hands. When I went to join them, I suddenly saw David. He smiled broadly at me with pride in his eyes. Pride for my courage and for what would come next.

"*Tira,* pull," the word came, and the crowd repeated wildly, "*Tira, tira!*" The strength of a united people went to work. Mexicans, Peruvians, Americans, Europeans, Africans, Koreans—men and women, big and small—worked in unison to tear down the wall, the barricade that protected the regime. Today the people were determined to tear down the oppression.

We pulled and pulled again. The fence tipped. And with a last surge of energy powerful enough to make an empire come down, the crowd pulled and the fence crashed onto the pavement.

The Koreans and *campesinos* negotiated a truce with the police, and instead of moving forward now that the barrier was gone, they asked us all to sit down. I moved to David's side. Once everyone was sitting, including the press, a deep silence in memory of Lee fell over the people. I put my head on David's shoulder and he wrapped his arm around me. The Koreans made a speech and handed out white flowers. Some people tried to march to the convention center after the speeches, but when the police pushed them back with their shields they returned peacefully and the crowd dispersed.

"You had me really worried," I said while we were heading to our tent. "Where were you?"

He gave me a quick rundown of his night adventure without sharing any details about the people he met with or the location of the meeting. When I asked for more specifics he said, "We're sworn to secrecy. All I can say was that we met at sacred ground and that the participants represented indigenous people and peasants from all continents. Things will change; we laid the foundation for a new world. The time for action is getting near."

"What do you mean by, 'the foundation for a new world'?"

"Last night we gave birth to the Gaia Confederation. It's probably best for your own safety to know no more."

"David, what are you involved in?" I insisted.

"God has shown me a way to make a bigger difference," he said. "That's all I can say."

Then he changed the subject and said, "I heard story after story of how corporate greed across the world leads to the demise of indigenous peoples. Did you know that every fortnight a language in the world disappears? Every two weeks the last person of a people takes a language and an entire culture to their grave. And every time that happens, this world loses some of its color, some of its true wealth, some of its magic and some of its capacity to recover from this globalization onslaught."

The next day we received good news. We had won! The WTO Ministerial Conference had collapsed when the Kenyans walked out. The Kenyans represented an entire group of African, Pacific and Caribbean nations in a "Green Room," which was a meeting with a smaller number of participants who represent larger groups of countries to work through the conference stumbling blocks. They decided there was no point in further talks since the U.S. and Europe refused to discuss their agricultural subsidy programs and the dumping of their grain in developing countries—something which was destroying the livelihoods of millions of subsistence farmers. The representatives of South Korea and India followed suit, and the Mexican Foreign Minister made it official shortly thereafter.

The people had won! There were celebrations at Ground Zero and all over Cancun where protestors were present. David smiled but wasn't exuberant. We had won this battle, but the struggle was far from over.

"There was a price for this victory," David said. "Lee's death served a purpose. We should be grateful for this victory. But it was only a small battle in a much bigger war for freedom. Establishing the Gaia Confederation will be a start to winning the war."

I wished to know more about this elusive Confederation he talked about, but knew that it would be pointless to ask more questions. I took solace in knowing that David was a good man who had been invited by indigenous and peasant leaders to join in the creation of a new foundation for the world. No doubt, time would reveal more.

SOARING EAGLE, LAKOTA ELDER

"'We did not inherit the earth from our ancestors; we borrow it from our children.' Those are the words of Tasunke Witko, Crazy Horse as you call him," I said to David as we sat together under a tree after a day of hard labor and watched the children play.

He had called me a few days after our first meeting in Cancun. I had invited him to attend a bison kill at the reserve in early October.

"The word for child in our language—*Wakanyeja*—means 'sacred gift,'" I continued my story. "For us Lakota, the children are the center of the Sacred Circle. They must be protected and nurtured because they are the future.

"We indigenous people from around the world do not understand the men of paper. They have contracts, words on paper for everything, and respect for nothing. With those words on paper they claim ownership of everything, and the right to forfeit respect for life. They claim the earth, water, seed and beast with a piece of paper. But how can one own the earth, any more than one can hold the air in one's hand? Men of paper steal the earth from the children.

They treat the earth not like their mother, but like an enemy to be conquered. Men of paper are at war with the earth and pillage the future of our children."

David had arrived early in the morning in Porcupine, a little village on the Pine Ridge Reservation where my home was. That day, we were receiving the sacred offer of the buffalo in preparation for a community feast the following day. The event was a celebration, a rite of passage, for some of our youth. It was organized by the families involved with the youth and children center here.

The center's goal is to provide our young people with roots and a purpose. They help us all to integrate aspects of our traditional life into this modern-day existence to nurture our culture and maintain our virtues of wisdom, bravery, generosity and fortitude. They teach us our language, which connects us with the land that provides for us. They teach us our culture, which connects us with our past. They teach us our spiritual ways, which connect us with Creator, with Mother Earth, with all creatures we share this existence with, and with our ancestors. They teach us to listen and search for a vision to guide our future.

Members of different families all joined together that morning and set out for the buffalo herd. There were men, women and children, and one white guy—David.

A young man had been prepared by the elders and medicine man for the sacred ritual: the making of the kill, the receiving of a life, the sacred gift of Tatanka who lives on in us. The young man had gone through a series of cleansing sweat lodges and fasted for four days, sleeping in the lodge at night.

The buffalo herd didn't roam freely across the lands as in the days of our ancestors. The U.S. government had parceled up our land and, under the usual strategy of divide-and-conquer, allocated a parcel to each of our families. After about a half hour drive by truck through rolling grasslands we spotted the grazing buffalo herd in their allocated half-section pasture.

The young man, an elder, two other band members and David were urged into the back of the pick-up truck which carefully approached the bison. The elder looked over the herd and identified the animal to be killed. Then we all watched as the young man took aim and waited for the marked bull to present himself for a good shot.

"Bang!" The noise echoed through soft glowing hills, and the well-placed shot dropped the animal on the spot. As with the loss of a family member, the herd gathered, almost in protection, around the fallen animal. It took us a while before we could move the grieving animals away from their brother.

The remaining band members and the women all gathered around the dead buffalo. The elder gave thanks to Creator and the buffalo people for the offer of life. Then we gutted the animal, loaded it in one of the trucks and brought it to a shed where we could butcher it in the coolness of the shade.

None of this was new to David. He had a herd of buffalo himself and was an avid hunter. So once the butchering began, he started skillfully skinning and de-boning the animal. He noticed a lot of the band members were uncertain about what to do, and was surprised to learn that attending a buffalo kill these days was a special occasion for Native Americans. The skills of gutting and butchering had been lost with the buffalo, and were only just now being reintroduced. It didn't take long before David was teaching both young men and old men how to cut the meat. He spent a lot of time working with my nine-year-old grandson, White Cloud, who had lost his father a few months ago. He held the child's hand with the knife and helped him to de-bone a hindquarter.

Without any reservation or intended blame, the young boy suddenly started a conversation that got everyone's attention.

"They told me in school your people killed all the buffalo. Why did you do that?" the boy asked with an innocence only children possess.

With compassion, David held White Cloud with his eyes. He softly smiled at the rest of us, showing he wasn't insulted or upset by the question. I was curious how he was going to answer.

"That's a good question," he said, demonstrating his interest while seeking more time to think.

"Not all my people killed the buffalo," he said. "If you ever come to my home, you'll see buffalo in the pastures as well. Killing all the buffalo wasn't a smart thing to do. But you have some dumb and ignorant people among every nation and every race, just like you have wise and caring people among every nation and every race."

The boy nodded his head.

"But what's done is done," David continued. "The question to ask now is, 'What do the buffalo teach us, and how can we make them return?'"

I could see the elders nodding in approval. This time the young boy was deep in thought. He had attended the kill in the morning, and together with his late father had looked after the herd in the past.

"Daddy told me Tatanka teaches us to share, like the animal whose meat we're cutting now has shared his life with us. We are to be grateful for that."

The boy spoke wisely beyond his years. I was a proud grandfather.

"But to let the buffalo return, we have to set them free," White Cloud said. "There's not enough grass on their pasture for the herd to become much bigger. Our teacher said that the buffalo herds during the time of our ancestors were as large as the eye could see. They can't grow their family strong and big if we keep them locked up in a fenced-off reservation just like us. They need to roam free."

More approving nods from the elders; more feelings of pride inside of me.

"But you might have to be careful that they don't leave the Pine Ridge," David said. "There might be people who would shoot them if they got outside."

"Then we should share our lands with the buffalo, like they share their lives with us," White Cloud said. "We should remove all the fences on the reservation and share the land as one family, one people—Lakota and buffalo, just like it used to be." The excitement rose in White Cloud's voice, and he added, "And then we can travel in teepees and stay with the herd. I love sleeping in a teepee, like we do during powwow." Then the boy took David's hand and said, "And you can always sleep in my teepee, Uncle David."

White Cloud's words and generosity touched everyone in the shed.

As we reflected on the day's events sitting in the shade, David asked, "How come the land on your reservation is all carved up in separate pastures like ours is? How come you didn't keep it all as communal lands?"

"If the choice had been ours, that's what would have happened," I said, grief in my heart. "The white man always found new ways to rob us of our lands. First they conquered it, then they made a peace treaty for which we received the great Sioux reservation, which stretched from the Missouri all the way beyond the Black Hills. It roughly comprised all of current South Dakota west of the Missouri river. Then they carved that up into smaller reservations under the threat of force so they could get gold from the Black Hills and put a railroad through the land.

"The Dawes Allotment Act was the next devious way under which they carved up the lands that were given to us and allotted them to the individual families of the bands, with the goal of further integration and breaking our communal culture. It was the end of hunting as a way of life. If that wasn't bad enough, they allocated those lands to a trust managed by the Bureau of Indian Affairs, and they only gave control of the land to persons whom they deemed capable of looking after their own land. Given the economic situation, the majority of our people who did receive control sold their land due to their impoverished situation, and the government sold and leased the lands they had in trust. In all we lost about two-thirds of the land base given to us under the treaty."

"I feel ashamed to belong to the people who have committed such treason," David said with sadness in his voice.

"You're not one of the paper men, David," I replied. "As you said earlier, deviousness is not determined by the color of a man's skin. This idea of land control belongs to a greedy category of men, men who continue today to rob people's land across the world. The piece of paper that gives someone property rights—the right to exclude others—is the most ridiculous injustice on our planet, and as long as it exists equality cannot."

White Cloud had burned off the majority of his young energy by now, and climbed onto David's lap as though he had known him for years.

"Mother Earth and our four-legged brothers and sisters teach us about freedom and equality," I said, satisfied to see that White Cloud was listening as well. "Take, for example, two fawns, born a world apart. One is born here on the plains, the other one somewhere in South America. Both fawns each will have a mother, and neither will ever know their father. Their mother will teach them where to find food and how to survive in the unique environment in which they are born. Their success in life is based on their genes and what they learn from their mother. It will determine how well they can survive in their environment and the breeding chances they'll get.

"Now, let's take two babies, born a world apart. One is born in a shanty town in South America, and the other is the son of one of the richest people on the planet. The first child has a mother and a father with no education and no access to any of the world's land. Day in, day out, the slum family struggles to feed their newborn child. As a result of the crib in which it is born, the child will have no access to any land, education, money or food.

"In contrast the child born in North America not only has access to any education, food, money and land he desires, he owns a significant portion of the planet's land and power, including the soil on which the first child was born."

"I see your point," David said.

But I wasn't done yet. "Now let's go back to the deer world to see how ridiculous this idea really is. If we apply the structures of our human society to the deer world, it would be the same as the King deer telling the peasant deer that it couldn't graze in the forest since the forest by right of birth belongs to the King deer which lives on another continent. But by the goodness of its heart the King deer offers the peasant deer an opportunity to run on a treadmill each day for which the King deer will provide the peasant deer a pile of daily hay. Now such a thing sounds totally ridiculous when we think of the deer world, right? So why is such a thing acceptable to most people when we talk of the human world? That's the part that indigenous people have never understood! How can anyone own the land?"

White Cloud jumped up and shouted, "Look at me, Uncle David!" The child threw himself onto the earth, arms open. "I can't grab it, I can't hold it." Then he jumped up and picked up a twig. "But I can hold this stick," he said with triumph in his eyes.

The boy had understood.

JOHN HOWARD, RETIRED FBI AGENT.

We knew David Green was up to something even though none of the people who were close to him had a clue. He had hit our radar in 2004 when we caught wind of an underground organization called, "The Gaia Confederation," a very secretive society with members from across the world.

It took us years to develop a clear profile due to their low-tech, I guess I should say, 'no-tech,' communication methods. They used personal couriers, handwritten notes and, you won't believe it, pigeon post. Pigeons, yes, but no emails, no cell phones, no chat, no websites and no credit cards.

David was not only a member; he was one of the founders.

We learned over the years that the organization was formed during an off-site meeting at the 2003 WTO meeting in Cancun. Like all secretive organizations, the Gaia Confederation wasn't officially incorporated anywhere.

We only got wind of it when an injured mail-pigeon landed at the farm of a Texas patriot. The man found the post message the bird was carrying, and thought it suspicious enough to inform the authorities. We like citizens that look out for their country. In cooperation with the farmer we nurtured the pigeon back to health, reattached the post package and implanted a rice-sized GPS tracking chip into the bird. The device tapped into the unlimited energy of its host through the application of bio-electronics and nanotechnology, allowing us to follow the bird for years. When we set it free the pigeon flew straight to David's farm.

The post message was written in code. It took our analyst some time to decipher it. What they got was enough for us to start tracking the organization. The pigeon led us to the messenger after it was shipped to carry the next post message. We covertly implanted chips into all of David's pigeons and those of each messenger we discovered. Slowly we uncovered the network.

But in the end, we did fail to prevent the first violent action of the Gaia Confederation. They mostly exchanged ideas for the creation of what they referred to as "living economies" and "a free borderless world with a network of diverse, locally oriented villages." Philosophical stuff, idealistic. You know, the kind of stuff that will never happen. Oh, yes, "returning power back to the people" was another one of those oft-mentioned phrases. People talk about such utopian dreams, and they might go as far as imagining people rallying behind their ideas, but the dreams will never happen. For one, such people don't know how to start creating such a world, and second, they don't have the courage to challenge the powerful forces that keep things running and maintain the status quo. Who pays me, do you think? Who writes the laws and pays armies? Most of the time such people only talk and set up harmless citizens' campaigns—some protest activities that never create any real change, and are mostly short-lived.

We only kept tabs on the Gaia Confederation because of their secrecy, and their unusual low-tech communications. We never discovered any signs of an imminent action, unfortunately.

Eva Green, David's Mother.

When David moved to the Black Hills, he started seeing this young woman, Kristen. I'm not sure I agreed with that relationship. But what could I say? He was a grown man. There wasn't really anything I could do, and I didn't want him to resent me or resist our visits. So I kept my mouth shut, but I didn't approve.

She turned my boy into an adventurer again. Once again he lost touch with the ways of the world, just like when he was eighteen. Suddenly he talked about these idealistic dreams again, like he was still a teenager.

He went looking for a farm in the Black Hills, and the next thing I knew he was flying to Cuba to learn about organic farming. To Cuba, of all places! What our Canadian farmers knew wasn't good enough anymore. He took off and left Tessa for three months with me. Well, I guess with Jody, but since she kept mostly to her bed mourning little Tom, I was the one who took care of Tessa.

When David bought his new farm in the Black Hills, he insisted that we didn't visit for almost a year.

"I want to clean the place up, Mother," he said. "The way this house is right now, there's nowhere for you to sleep, and I'm too busy fixing up the house and building the farm. There's just no time for visitors."

I'm not sure if that was really my son talking or this new woman who had entered his life. Instead he came and brought Tessa for the summer vacation that year, and came to visit us at Thanksgiving.

When we drove down there the following year, Kristen was more or less living there. During the week she stayed at her own place since it was more convenient for work, but most every time when we visited on weekends or for Thanksgiving or Christmas, she would be there. She could almost be his daughter, that's how young she was. He seemed happy, but their relationship just didn't feel right to me.

Tessa called her, "Auntie Kristen." What an example for that little girl! David told me Kristen was only a friend, a good friend who helped out and made things much easier for Jody. And Jody didn't seem to mind. But she was also in a state where she didn't mind anything anymore. And for all he said, a mother knows better. I could see how they looked at each other. I even saw how she touched his hand once.

But what could I say with all the hardship he had gone through? I have to admit, Kristen was a friendly and polite woman and Tessa was fond of her. The first year David allowed us to come, we visited four times. Over the years it dwindled down to once or twice, usually for Thanksgiving, Christmas or Tessa's birthday.

I could see how my son was changed. He became more radical when he returned from this farmers' protest in Mexico. I think Kristen got him involved with the wrong people, and they all poisoned his mind. I found out it was she who had suggested he go to Cuba as well, and she had joined him for those protests in Mexico.

Kristen was a rebellious woman. David once told me she participated in this big protest march in Seattle; you know, the one where they burned cars and broke all those store windows. Yeah, what can I say? She was trouble. Quite different from Jody, who was such a good wife and mother until poor Tom took her heart into his grave.

Ever since David came back from Mexico he didn't seem to have any time for us anymore. He was always busy; either it was the farm that needed his time, or he was studying, or making visits to this Indian reservation, or working on a campaign to change the world.

"Mom, I finally found a way to make things better for other children so that boys like Tom don't have to die, and so that parents like Jody and me don't have to live with the knowledge that we contributed to the death of our child," he said. "I'm sure you understand how important it is for me to make sure something positive flows from Tom's death!"

And so our visits became shorter and were reduced to just once a year. I tried to call him at least every other month just to hear his voice and talk with Tessa. I did notice during our visits and phone conversations that he was growing much more political. He was always talking about how corporations had taken over the world and ruined democracy. As for me, I never cared too much for politics.

"We have to organize to change this system," he said to me.

And as a mother, I could only think about all those brave and good men in history who had organized a mass of people, who had encouraged people to stand up, and how they had all been killed. So it scared me, when David talked like that. I had already lost a grandson, and I wasn't ready to lose my son as well. Why could he not simply concentrate on his organic farm? That was a good thing. It made a difference, and allowed him to feed his family without painting a target on his back.

I think all his political ideas were how he got himself in trouble.

ANONYMOUS, ORGANIC FARMER.

"Mr. David Green," the older of the two men in black suits said, "we have evidence that you are using Empuro's proprietary seed on your farm without the company's permission."

It was a Saturday evening in the spring of 2004, and my family was visiting the Greens at Crazy Horse Fields. We were having supper together. We had just finished our prayer when the doorbell rang and David's world changed again. It seemed that this company, which had already taken the life of his son, didn't feel it had got enough from David yet.

"Mr. Green, you are in violation of the company's intellectual property rights. In other words, you're stealing. Now, we can do this the easy way and you can sign these papers here and agree to pay the technology fees, the price for the seed, and compensation for the infringement and for the cost the company incurred in hiring us. Or we can do this the painful way: Empuro can take you to court, which will mean that after one or two years, with you having paid hundreds of thousands of dollars in legal fees, the judge will fine you for the infringement. The sum will likely exceed what's proposed here in these documents, and you will also have to reimburse Empuro for the army of lawyers they will have paid to prove that you were stealing.

"Beware Mr. Green, Empuro is a very powerful company with the best lawyers money can buy. They will make your life, and of course that of your family, a hell for the next few years until you comply. They never lose lawsuits. They will start with demanding access to every little piece of paper that is part of your farm business. They will use those documents to contact all your clients and suppliers to verify if they were involved in processing, selling or buying your illegal crop. If they were, they too will be legally pursued. So we suggest you sign here, Mr. Green."

The men were accompanied by two police officers who were watching the scene from the driveway. David stood speechless at the door.

When David finally found his tongue, he collected himself and said, "There must be a mistake. I'm sure you have the wrong farm. I don't buy their seed; I run an organic farm."

"So you're going to resist. I would not advise that, sir!" the same man said. He stepped closer to David and in a subdued voice— just like that of a friend who is providing some profound advice— added, "Empuro is not a company to mess with, Mr. Green. Look around here; you have a nice farm, so if I were you I would sign here, or all this land will be owned by another more cooperative farmer in a couple of years when you have to sell due to insurmountable legal fees or bankruptcy. The new owner will buy Empuro's genetically modified seed, spray their fertilizers, herbicides and pesticides, and pay their technology fees. Think about your effort of running an organic farm for years; it will all be for nothing when the next guy starts spraying pesticides. I know it's expensive, but you broke the law and have to pay the consequences. So if you want to keep your farm and livelihood, I would say signing here is a smart investment."

David was a man who hardly ever lost his temper. I had never seen him lose control. This time though I could see him tense up. He was ready to explode. It was Kristen who came to the rescue.

She got up, walked through the door like the men weren't even there, and went straight to the policemen.

"Do you have an arrest warrant or a search document?" she asked.

"Uh no," the officer replied, visibly upset at being pulled into the conversation.

"Mr. Green, your wife is making a big mistake. You're going to regret this. I suggest you call her back," the first man said.

Kristen knew the local officer and continued, "Dale, tell me, what are you doing here playing pit bull for these men who are falsely accusing David? Please escort them off our property as their company is unwelcome and they're now trespassing."

She turned around, walked through the door, grabbed the papers from the man with the black suit without acknowledging his existence, guided David by the shoulder into the room and slammed the door behind her.

I tell you, that day Kristen earned my deepest respect.

David was growing Canola in the new field he had acquired the year before. I just wished he had listened to me and stayed away from the major crops that the powerful seed corporations are trying to control through their genetically modified technology. You know— corn, soy and Canola. He brought the seeds with him from Canada when he moved here, and had all the paperwork to prove it. The Canola variety was developed by his father who had never wanted anything to do with the seed corporations, and like all farmers of old, stuck to the principle of seed saving and barter among colleagues.

Empuro claimed they had collected samples from David's field, which proved their proprietary Canola was being grown on his land.

I don't know if a different reaction from Kristen would have made a difference, but like the man had said, over the following year Empuro turned the life of David's family into a living hell, once again.

A week after the visit a registered letter arrived from a law firm demanding all David's records of seed purchases and other farm expenses.

Kristen told David he didn't have to hand over anything without a search warrant. Then the lawyers referred to a document David had allegedly signed in Canada years ago when he purchased products from Empuro. It gave the company the right at any time to demand access to such data. When David denied that he had ever signed such a document, they produced one with a forged signature. When David's lawyers protested the forged signature, some legal mumbo jumbo was presented as grounds to reject the evidence of the forgery. The demand for information was upheld.

Empuro offered several times to settle out of court, but David steadfastly refused.

"Why would I agree to pay anything for something I didn't do?" he said. "I will explain my case to the judge, and I'm sure that once the court looks at all the evidence that I'll be acquitted."

David had taken counter samples of the Canola growing in his field. Toward the center of the field, barely any Canola plants were contaminated by the genetically modified gene. However, both sides of the field that bordered the road and along the side of the adjacent field where a neighbor grew Empuro's Canola, there was clear contamination by Empuro's proprietary gene.

Canola is pollinated by bees. Bees are not aware of fences, nor do they understand the proprietary nature of one plant versus another. Given the partial and localized contamination of David's field, it was reasonable to assume that some seed had blown in from the trucks and equipment of his neighbor when passing David's field, and that the bees had practiced cross-pollination and fertilized some of David's field with the pollen of Empuro's Canola.

David was encouraged by another farmer up in Canada who had challenged another large multinational seed corporation on the same grounds.

"Here's what I don't get," he said. "If they can't contain their proprietary gene to fields where it was seeded, they should be paying *me*. It's my field that's contaminated with their technology which I didn't buy, don't want and can't sell. I lost my entire crop and income from that field."

Talking about it sure made him mad. Frankly, I'm no lawyer, but when the wind or bees can spread Empuro's technology onto someone's land and that gives them ownership over the crop that grows there and provides grounds for a lawsuit, I'd say things are seriously messed up. It should be the other way around; the company should be liable for not being able to contain their product and for the biological pollution it causes. With the current laws, they can count on the bees to do their work, and gradually put all farmers who don't buy from them out of business until they control the entire industry.

"Did you know Empuro employs an entire legal department of over one hundred people, and hires private detective firms to harass farmers like us?" David said during the year the lawsuit was ongoing. "They have an entire department of people that use threats and legal pressure to discourage farmers from saving their seeds. And they don't just have it out for organic farmers, but also for conventional farmers, seed processors, co-ops and seed sellers who don't use their genetically modified seed. I contacted some other farmers who are going through the same ordeal. A few guys referred to these thugs who do the company's dirty work as the 'Gestapo.' It's outrageous that things like this happen in our country, the land of the free."

Throughout the lawsuit David's mood would swing. One day he would be ready to shoot everyone who worked for Empuro, and the following day, he had regained his calmness again, was putting his trust in the legal system, and had found inspiration in some texts from Oscar Romero, the Archbishop of San Salvador whom he had known years ago.

"If I hadn't known this man and witnessed the honor and peaceful power with which he struggled for the poor, I think I might have given up a long time ago and been sucked into the violence that pervades this world," David shared with me one day.

Then he read some words from Romero which he compared to his legal struggle: "I will not tire of declaring that if we really want an effective end to violence we must remove the violence that lies at the root of all violence: structural violence, social injustice, exclusion of citizens from the management of the country, repression. All this is what constitutes the primal cause, from which the rest flows naturally."

KRISTEN SMITH, ENVIRONMENTALIST.

In the summer of 2005 a verdict was given. David was found guilty and charged with one million two hundred thousand dollars in damages and court fees.

David had already mortgaged everything he had to fund his David-versus-Goliath battle. The verdict left him psychologically wounded and economically without choice; he had to declare bankruptcy. The entire estate went up for auction. When the sun rose the morning of the sale, David walked outside and took the two frames above the door down and put the pictures again in his breast pocket. "I don't want those boys to see how their legacy is being torn to bits today," he said, defeat in his words. "I'll keep them close to my heart again. It seems to be the only place where they are safe in this world."

When the farm auction was over, the land, equipment and most of his family's belongings sold, he sat broken next to me on his favorite bench on the porch. The bench now belonged to one of the neighbors who had bought it, but had agreed to leave it there for another week.

For the entire day of the auction, David had turned as cold as ice. When friends and neighbors came over to offer their sympathy, he simply shook his head and walked away. He couldn't speak.

I moved closer, put my arms around him and stroked his hair. The physical touch was enough to break through his armor, and the emotional floodgates burst open. My strong man wept in silence with an occasional subdued, heart-wrenching moan.

"What have I done? How can I face Jody and Tessa? Once again I've failed to take care of my family. I should have just paid the bastards and accepted that men of injustice rule this world of living paper and dying hearts," he whispered when he'd caught his breath.

The man in the black suit had been right; another farmer bought the land for a bargain and then, like a loyal servant, seeded Empuro's seed on it the following year.

In Cancun I had realized that the day we would consummate our love might never come. I had planned to distance myself from the family. I would still be their friend; however, I couldn't keep investing my love in a man who might never return it in full. But when the suit started I delayed my decision. And now that a judgment was made, David needed me more than ever. How could I leave him now?

David was a mess during the month that followed, when they stayed in a trailer at a neighbor's field. During this time though, Jody tried to reach for the world and break from her self-created prison. I could see it when she embraced David, how her eyes forgave him, and how at times she softly stroked his back. As hard as she had been hurt, she still carried David in her heart. And so I hoped this tragedy would trigger Jody to come to life again and allow her to share her love.

David blamed himself yet again for failing to care for his family. He was confused, and saw no way forward. His conscience and promise to Tom left him no option to function within a system that poisoned the world, that pursued digital numbers on a bank account at the real cost of children's lives. But when he tried to do the right thing, and demonstrate the success of a sustainable farming operation, the laws in the country were stacked against him.

"The founders of this country, and all those who have spilled their blood for it, would roll over in their graves if they knew that the constitution is now being used to protect the rights of lords and kings in faraway ivory towers, hidden behind fictitious entities called 'corporations,' destroying the liberty of ordinary hardworking citizens and preventing anyone from pursuing any other dream than the dream of the king," he said. "The lawmakers in this country have made a mockery of the values on which this republic is based."

"Then we should start campaigning to change those laws," I suggested in the hope of helping him find a new purpose again so he could move beyond his current state of hopelessness.

"Campaigning for something assumes the powers of democracy are functioning," David responded. "They stopped functioning when fictitious entities like corporations became legal persons with the same rights as people of flesh and blood. It might be more effective to take up arms, just like the founders of this country did when they realized that the laws of Britain were legalizing the actions of thieves, and enslaved honest working people to the whims of a greedy super-elite with an insatiable lust for power, luxury and control."

"David, we're living in a democracy now," I countered.

"Democracy is a scam," he said, and I could feel he was climbing out of his state of desperation, but with his heart turning to stone again. It reminded me of the coldness in his eyes when we met in the Black Hills after Tom's death. Over the years, the land, and I'd like to think our love, had softened his soul. David had found joy and happiness in ordinary things. He believed he was actively making a difference, and had developed an interest in changing things through democratic citizen movements and peaceful action. But the song of revenge had grabbed control of his heart once again. The difference now was that he had studied the system and the impact of corporate power in the world a great deal more. If he was going to act beyond the law, this time it would be calculated to achieve a strategic goal.

"Corporations can't die a natural death; they are not of flesh and blood. As a result they can accumulate money and assets over generations in the name of the faceless legal fictions they are, never to reveal their true puppet masters. Their wealth creates a disproportionate advantage in the marketplace, and they use that power unscrupulously, similar to the Gestapo-like practices of Empuro in their relentless pursuit of wealth and power. At this point the majority of the world resources are controlled by these faceless fictions, which is why all of us find it necessary to run on their treadmill so we can feed our families.

"Corporations have no conscience; a legal fiction cannot have a conscience. But they also can't be put in jail, nor do we ever put them to death for violating the law. That's how the puppet masters can get away with murder. But we do give corporations the same rights as every natural person without any mention of their personhood in the constitution. On top of it all, when their economic health is being threatened due to mismanagement, our government uses our taxes to fund them as we're told they are 'too big to fail.'"

"But it's the people who vote; we elect our leaders in this country," I said.

"You think we do," David countered again. "But the media is controlled by corporations, which means they have the power to shape the way we think twenty-four-seven. And corporations are using their funds and creativity not only to elect leaders in office that benefit the corporations' interests, but they also spend billions of dollars to influence lawmakers to the benefit of their goals. And what voice do we, the citizens, have in all this when we're competing against billion-dollar corporations that have the same rights as you or me? You guessed it! Our rights are annihilated.

"They like us to think we have a voice, so they feed us issue-related causes, like animal rights, or organic food, or water sovereignty, but in doing that they divide and conquer. They dilute the power of the masses by focusing them on symptoms and distracting them from the common structural cause—the fact that corporations are recognized as legal persons with the same rights as you and me. If, as a citizens' movement, we are ever going to be successful, we first need to take our democracy back. And that means recognizing corporations for what they are supposed to be—legal fictions called to life for the execution of a specific and defined economic goal. They should never be more.

"Did you know that a number of food corporations are now lobbying for a new law that will make it illegal for anyone to make their production methods public or criticize their practices?

"Let me tell you, Kristen, it is money that rules the world, not democracy. Democracy is only a scam; it's a make-believe freedom, and its only purpose is to keep the mass of people quiet so that the super-elite can continue to plunder the world right from under our noses."

I knew that what he was saying was true, but I never wanted to acknowledge it because it was too depressing a reality. Recognizing it also required me to reassess the effect of citizen activism and the things I was spending my life on.

"Instead of democracy, we have corporatism, which means that a small group of people in the world can use your money to advance their interest," David went on.

I stayed silent. David was becoming ever more agitated and angry as he kept on ranting. I wanted him to stop, but how do you stop such a wounded man? How was I to comfort him by arguing?

So the only thing I said was, "You're right; we live in a messed-up world."

By the end of the summer Soaring Eagle invited David to join him for a meeting in Guatemala with the same secret group of people they met with when we were in Cancun.

"Why would I come?" David questioned.

"Because of your insights and because you care," Soaring Eagle said.

"But it's all no use. This movement for social justice has been losing ground for more than a century," David said. "What's the use of another movement?"

"Well if that's your choice, so be it," Soaring Eagle answered. "But I thought you were tougher than that. Remember what my people went through; remember the circumstances we live in today. And I tell you what, we're still here! We're still fighting for a better world, and we'll do so till our last breath. It's the example that was set by our ancestors. It's the way of Crazy Horse. You lived on his land, so ask yourself what Crazy Horse would do and let his spirit touch your soul."

David was quiet for a while, then said, "So when are we leaving?"

SOARING EAGLE, LAKOTA ELDER.

The calls of the Howler Monkeys announced the sunrise. The jungle, like any other forest in the world, is most active during the twilight time.

We had left our rooms concealed in the darkness of the night and hiked silently, in single file, through a black living void. By the time the sun rose, there were close to a hundred of us, indigenous and peasant leaders from across the planet, facing east on top of Temple IV, the largest pyramid of the Mayan ruins of Tikal in the Guatemalan rainforest. From our high vantage point we could see several other ruins emerge from the forest canopy in their apparent reach for the sky.

A Mayan shaman led us in prayer to honor the light and power of the sun. Unlike the previous gathering which was guided by the moon, this meeting of the leaders of the Gaia Confederation took place at a time when day and night were in perfect harmony, the fall equinox. It was also a time that announced a coming time of darkness. The meeting would take place under the guidance of the sun. The setting of this once majestic capital of the Mayan civilization was chosen for a reason.

When the prayers ended, the Mayan medicine man stretched his arm out over the forest.

"See the magnificence of this jungle, the vibrant energy and teeming life. It took only a few generations for Earth to heal Herself. Once upon a time more than one million people lived and worked here for a thousand years to create a foolish dream of grandeur and power for a small elite. Look at it now. We are sitting on top of the most important temple of that civilization, and now it is a mere ruin in the landscape. I brought you here so you can see what the inevitable outcome is of a society whose laws don't respect the laws of Pachamama, the Great Mother. This has been the fate and always will be the fate of any society that tries to conquer Earth instead of honoring Her and living in harmony with the living universe."

We all pondered the words of the medicine man. The point was well made and set the tone for the conversation of the circle that followed. After sunrise we climbed down and moved to the Temple of the Lost World. Clearly this was done partly for practical reasons, since the platform on top facilitated the forming of a circle meeting. But it had also been chosen because of its symbolism of the lost world which we tried to bring to life again, a world that recognized the power of Mother Earth and functioned in harmony with it.

Word of the Gaia Confederation had spread among the oppressed of this world—society's lost citizens. The large number of people also meant a long meeting with many different perspectives and ideas.

"I wonder how civilizations in the past crumbled?" a man from an island tribe in the Pacific said. "For generations, my people have bled, been used as slaves, and died at the whims of barbarians. Now they're building some kind of chemical plant whose effluents will destroy our entire reef and our fishing waters for generations to come. On top of all that, the waters of the sea are rising, threatening the coastal lands that have been home to my people. When is enough,

enough? I know Mother Earth will prevail, but when will we start helping her? Frankly, without a future for my children, I feel like blowing up this chemical plant."

In circle meetings like this, led by respected elders, people stood and spoke from the heart while everyone listened. There was always some time for silence before the next person spoke. It was a time when everyone was digesting and taking to heart the words spoken by their fellow brother or sister.

"History has taught us that violence has never brought a solution," an elder from Colombia said. "We know the cruelty of modern man. We see it every day around us as people across the planet are being tortured and nature is being destroyed. But in past times when we used violence as a method for resistance, we only unleashed more brutal repercussions and Earth didn't fare any better for it. Only our families suffered. I don't know when Mother Earth is going to decide that enough is enough, but I think only She has the power to bring modern man to reason. Only She is powerful enough to stop the wave of destruction."

"If someone is killing your mother and you watch it happen without taking any action to save her, does that make you complicit to her killing?" a Frenchman asked.

"But when is self-defense, self-defense?" David asked. "I can see when someone attacks my family and know how I would act in self-defense. But is it self-defense if I fight back when someone slowly poisons my family and keeps putting restraints on our way of life to an extent where it becomes impossible to make a living without becoming an accomplice to their crime of destroying Mother Earth?"

"My people have walked both the path of the tomahawk and the path of peace," I said. "No matter which path we walked, we were no better off. War often brought a quick death and a short life for our families, but we roamed free, lived as we believed we should and experienced the intensity of existence. Peace allowed our families to live longer, but within a caged world that killed the spirit of our people and dulled the experience of life.

"At the end of the day, I think we need to do what our soul tells us to do. For some that will be to care for their families and accept the bondage placed upon them; for others it will be to peacefully resist and take solace in slow change and times in jail; and for others again it will be to fight for their freedom, to strategically destroy the structures that allow the emperors of the modern culture to stay in place. And then there will be those for which the means is to aim directly at the leadership itself. We cannot judge the path taken by our fellow brothers; we can only recognize our common goal. It's up to each one of us to choose what works for us; only we know what our role must be in the changes to come. And likely, to achieve our goal, we might need brothers and sisters to walk each of those paths."

The circle was called to a close when the sun set. We didn't come much further ahead in defining what the Gaia Confederation was about and how to move forward. This day was about sharing our different views and giving thought to what was being said.

As we walked back, a struggle was raging inside of David about his role in these changing times.

"How do we know what to do? How do we know our purpose and role in bringing about the changes the elders and shamans are talking about?" David asked me as we walked through the jungle to our living quarters.

"That's the funny thing about men," I said. "A beaver would never ask such a question. A beaver knows it's a beaver and builds dams. A deer knows it's a deer and populates the forest with its offspring to graze the forest floor. A parasite knows what it is and enjoys life as long as it can feed on its host. And a mountain lion acts like the king of the world; it keeps the deer population from spreading to a point where they kill the undergrowth of the forest, and it prevents the bacteria from spreading through an entire herd, by killing the sick animal and the parasite with it. We never judge the deer for being deer or the cougar for being cougar.

"But man doesn't know his role because he can choose from all of the above. And man is quick to judge other fellow human beings for their action or inaction when it doesn't fit his vision. Man has been given choice; it's been both his blessing and his curse. What are we to do?

"Modern man uses his mind to search for the answer and will never find it, as purpose is never rational or calculated. It must be felt in the bones, be revealed by the heart, or discovered in the depths of the soul. That's why all indigenous people in the world have their version of what we Lakota call the 'vision quest.' It's a time when we travel the depths of our soul, feel what's in our bones, and allow our heart to speak. It's a time when we open ourselves up to the guidance of Creator.

"I suggest you spend some time in the mountains and observe if the beaver, deer or cougar appear from your heart. Then you'll know what to do."

JOHN HOWARD, RETIRED FBI AGENT.

It was hard to get a handle on the Gaia Confederation. First off, since they didn't use any electronic communication technology, we couldn't eavesdrop on anything. And even though we were able to follow the pigeons through the GPS implants, it only gave us the locations they were flying from. The confederation's network also continuously expanded, as pigeons were shipped to different locations we didn't know about yet.

However, we did discover another reason for their low-tech communication systems. Some of the birds were shipped to remote locations where there wasn't even a telephone line. At first this relaxed us a bit. We thought that the pigeons were more a practical method of communication, instead of having an ultra-secret purpose. It confirmed the idea of many of the guys in the office, those who didn't believe that a bunch of pipe-smoking and dart-blowing Indians and bush men could be a threat to the world order.

And so we became less concerned about the challenges their primitive communication systems had presented us with, namely, following their old-fashioned air-mail didn't give us access to the mail package that was flying with it. Short of shooting the bird from the air, it provided a real problem in terms of intercepting their communication. Since we knew about David's involvement and he was right here in the U.S., we decided to focus on him. We figured that if there was a threat to homeland security, it was going to come from the inside. So every time we detected a pigeon in flight to David's farm, our field agents had to sneak into his place, find the right bird in his pigeon coop, take a copy of the message and reattach it so our interception would go unnoticed.

We also kept taps on conversations David had with other members of the Gaia Confederation here in the United States. That was the easy part of the operation, since there was only one other person involved here. His name was Jack Two Birds, but he called himself "Soaring Eagle." He lived at the Pine Ridge Reservation—and that in itself was a red flag, as we all remember the trouble those

Indians caused at Wounded Knee in the early seventies. We learned most about the threat the new organization formed from the conversations we tapped into between David and Soaring Eagle.

When David lost his farm, we thought he would be defeated and finally give up on his idealistic views of the world and step into place just like most everyone else. But we were wrong. Either David was a real stubborn guy with a resilience that allowed him to crawl back onto his feet time and time again, or the Gaia Confederation had a most effective brainwashing program.

During the months that followed David's bankruptcy, the communication between the two men clearly radicalized. David was asking Soaring Eagle if violence could have a function in creating a new world. He started to talk about the eradication of corporate power. Suddenly all corporations seemed to be evil in his mind.

People often come to such narrow conclusions when life throws them a curve ball. The man gets caught stealing, and suddenly the corporation which only claims what is rightfully theirs is the bad one. In David's case, he took an even further leap; suddenly all corporations were bad entities. I guess he forgot who provided the gas for his vehicle or the truck he was driving. Yeah, most people don't ever think about the good stuff, even though they all enjoy it and benefit from it. Tell me, who do you think creates all the jobs in the world? Corporations, right? That's true even of my job; if all the people in this country didn't have some form of income on which to pay taxes, and if we didn't collect corporate taxes, there would be no money to pay me. I tell you, corporations pay for our rent, food and clothing—even our charities that take care of society's needs! I never saw what was wrong with that.

Before my job with the FBI, I was a private security agent, and we would often be contracted as bodyguards for corporate big-shots.

And granted, some have attitudes. But you know what? They deserved their place among the wealthy in the world. They could afford to have an attitude. But most of them were nice guys, real polite and friendly. And they paid well. I would have taken a bullet for them any day. People like that aren't someone to be angry with; instead they're an example and an inspiration as to what to strive for.

The only challenge for us with the communication between David and Soaring Eagle was that Indians, like most natives across the world, aren't capable of giving a direct answer. No simple "yes" or "no" here. Instead they say something like, "When you're a deer, act like a deer; when you're a wolf, act like a wolf." What was that supposed to mean? If it were only some code, then at least we could decipher it to something that made sense. But in this case we always had to guess what Soaring Eagle really meant. Then we had to guess again how David could have interpreted it.

But one thing was clear: when David asked if the use of violence was justifiable, Soaring Eagle never said, "No." So we paid closer attention.

EVA GREEN, DAVID'S MOTHER.

When David lost the farm he was angry. I had seen him lost when he returned from El Salvador, I had seen him grieving after Tom died, but I had rarely seen my son angry.

His anger raged against corporate power in general, but also against the corruptness and greed within our culture which, according to him, made a mockery of democracy.

"You know, Mother, this culture of domination and drive for power has been ongoing for some two to three thousand years, and it has infected this planet now from the deepest rainforest to the highest mountains," he told me one day. "At first the power mongers used religions to control people's freedom; if you look at all those cultures that vanished with time, their temples and churches were the monuments that dominated their societies. Today, it's the towers of banks and corporations that rise high above any other building in the world to indicate the power of money and the corporate logo.

"For thousands of years no one dared to challenge the rulers and their priests about the word of God, and who today is brave enough to question the value and ways of money? Science provided a window for people to question certain aspects of religion and take some of their spiritual power back. So the rulers needed a new way to maintain control. That point in history is marked by the breakdown of the commons and the rise and power of capital. And whoever questions the soundness of capitalism and money today is branded a 'communist'—the equivalent of 'witch' during the time of the Inquisition; the worst possible sinner to be stoned or burned at the stake without trial."

I'm not sure where he got all these ideas from; I never heard him talk like that before! The people he socialized with had changed. He traveled to Mexico and Guatemala and spent time with those he called, "indigenous elders and peasant leaders; people with the wisdom of Mother Earth." To me it sounded like the poor people of this world. David had gone back to where he had started when he left high school. But to be successful in this world, he needed to surround himself with people who were rich and well-off. But how could I blame him, after the price he had paid?

A lot of his anger was focused on this evil corporation, Empuro. And they are evil! He sure had a right to be angry with them. They took my grandson away from me and then stole my son's farm, Tessa's home.

When Tom died, David tried to forgive the company, or maybe he considered that Tom might have gotten the cancer from somewhere else. That scenario was of course an attractive one for him, since it also meant he wasn't to blame for spraying their chemicals on his fields. Not that he ever said anything like that, but I always thought something like this might have gotten into his mind, given the way he was able to move on with life.

It was only when Empuro took Crazy Horse Fields from him that David realized the ingrained evil nature of this company. I don't think the loss of his farm was the cause of his rage; it only helped to direct it. The real source of it was Tom's death.

When Crazy Horse Fields was sold, David found a small cheap piece of land, just a few acres, along a nice creek west of Sheridan, Wyoming. We lent him some money to buy it. He pulled our trailer out there, and during the summer of 2005 that's where they lived while David built a cabin for the family to move into before winter.

I prayed that he would find a new purpose, once again. A man needs to have a goal in order to move on with life and care for his family.

When I asked David what his plans for the future were, he said, "Well, Mother, it isn't really much different from before, other than now, everything is much clearer in my mind. I'm going to care for my family and reduce my own footprint on this planet by practicing permaculture."

"Permaculture?"

"It is a way of living that respects permanence, sustainability and culture. The goal is to design a way of life that is rooted in the local environment, doesn't destroy this world, and is economically viable in that it allows a family to provide for its own needs."

"Sounds like the way we used to live in the olden days," I said, relieved that he seemed to have found a new path again. "You're saying it more fancy, but I think that's how we used to live. Going back to the old ways is a sound thing to do, my son."

"But it's not enough," he added. "See, the problem with our culture of globalization is that it infects and poisons any culture that has lived sustainably with the use of permaculture designs for tens of thousands of years. And the infection keeps on spreading. It's like a virus that keeps on feeding on its host until it devours it. When part of a crop is infected with a disease, Empuro teaches us to spray it and kill it or it will spread and infect the entire crop. It's time for us to protect ourselves against this virus that is spreading through the world and kill it before there isn't anything left to save!"

There was a dark shadow in David's eyes when he said that— something I hadn't seen before. My concern wasn't with society. Rather, I was afraid that the heartless evil of this corporation had infected my son's soul.

I decided to pray for David to help him find his way to the light again.

FATHER JACK MARSHAL, PASTOR.

"Father," David said, "Why do you preach? Why did you choose your path to serve God?"

David had come to visit me shortly after he attended the first service in our community. This wasn't anything unusual for new parishioners. But his question took me by surprise. It was direct and personal, even though his demeanor was friendly. I think he wanted to gauge my intentions to understand the sincerity of my path.

"Because I love Him," I said. "I know His power and His love. When I can share that love and bring people closer to Him, when I can help them see the light and walk in His footsteps, then I contribute my little piece in bringing the Kingdom of Heaven to earth.

"Jesus offered His life for our salvation. He offered His life so we would find His way. Putting my life in His service is my sacrifice to the path of Love which He showed us."

I hadn't thought about why I had joined the seminary for decades, and I found it quite unusual for a newcomer in the community to ask such a question. Come to think of it, I don't think anyone had ever asked me this before. In truth, I was kind of glad someone did. Answering the question made me reflect on how I had fallen into this rut over the last few decades of doing my job as prescribed by the Church. It made me realize how the passionate zeal that accompanied me in my early years as a priest had escaped me. Had I lost my path? Was I still serving the way of Love?

"Father, I can tell you're a good man and have chosen your path with the best intentions," David said.

I wasn't clear where he was heading, but it was most unusual for a parishioner to say something like that. People don't question the goodness of priests and holy men; it is taken for a fact, and so such things are never mentioned.

Then David continued, "Your sermon in mass was about the seven woes of the Pharisees, the hypocrites as Jesus called them. You read Matthew 23:23-28, the part saying 'like whitewashed tombs, beautiful on the outside, but full of dead man's bones' was very relevant to the events that brought me to this community. But then you merely touched on the importance of 'walking the path of Jesus' and that was the end of it. You could have done so much more with that passage.

"You must read the news; you must know what goes on in the world. Yet the same people who commit injustices in the highest offices in corporations and governments around the world, often visit church every Sunday to cleanse their soul, 'like whitewashed tombs, beautiful on the outside, but full of dead man's bones.'

"Why didn't you bring the gospel home to today's world? Make it relevant. Point out what the path of the Pharisees is in today's world. It would have been so much more powerful and truly helped people stay on course and walk Jesus' path of Love."

I didn't quite know what to say. In truth, I knew he was right. I also realized that I had entered the seminary to preach exactly like that. In a way I was no different from the charity worker who ends up filling out forms for grants instead of saving lives, or the businessman who ends up chasing profits instead of serving the needs of customers, or the couple settling for a routine marriage instead of the passion of love. But when did I lose my passion? When did I fall into such routine? And then I remembered how I came to be this way.

"David, I appreciate your question and insight. And I know that what you say is true. But if I were to talk like you suggest, my church would be empty. So I choose to tell the story of Jesus in the hope some of the souls in my parish can relate those stories in their own way to their own lives."

"And when you look at the world today, Father, do you think this way of preaching is working?"

Why did he have to poke further? Why had God sent me this man? Was there any reason for me to look into the mirror?

"Father, I don't want to make you uncomfortable," he said and relieved me of answering. "I once knew a priest who inspired me like no one else ever has. He was a living example of the way of Jesus. I saw that quality in you during mass, and I need someone who speaks truth, who demonstrates and reminds us that the path of Love is a living path. I need someone I can hold onto, as I feel I might be slipping away into the dark shadows of my soul."

Then David told me about his time in El Salvador and about Archbishop Romero. I had heard of him, but had never taken the time to learn more about him or read any of his sermons.

"Monsignor Romero showed the way. to a living spiritual path," David said, "a path that was guided by Jesus on a daily basis, a path reflected in how we act, and not in who we pray to or when and where we worship. I've written down some of his words, and would gladly share them with you if you're interested." David handed me the following words of the Archbishop of San Salvador, Oscar Romero:

What use is it to have beautiful churches if Jesus were to proclaim to us today the same words that he spoke to the Pharisees: "in vain do you worship me." Yes, we might celebrate elaborate worship services, with many flowers and other adornments, with many people invited to participate in the celebration, but where is the worship in Spirit and truth? I believe there is a lesson here for us and so my sisters and brothers, I am the first one to receive it and attempt to interpret it. Perhaps I, as a priest, have not known how to fulfill in a proper way my duties involving the worship of God. Perhaps I and my brother priests have been too concerned about the beautiful arrangement of the altar and perhaps I have asked for money in order to have the altar more beautifully decorated. We have commercialized our worship. Therefore God, as though entering Jerusalem with a whip tells us, "My house shall be a house of prayer but you are making it a den of thieves." We all have to stop and think. We are all guilty.

David helped me find my path and passion again. I stuck the piece of paper with those words against my door so each time now when I walk into the world, they remind me about what it means to serve God and be a living example of His way.

KRISTEN SMITH, ENVIRONMENTALIST.

"Love is my savior," David told me one day in the spring of 2006. He had shown me how the seeds in his organic garden were germinating before we sat together on the bench by the creek. "I had a lot of time to think over the winter about last year's events. I sat on the bench under the weeping willow here by the creek and marveled at the white crystals that fell from the sky and covered the earth in a protective blanket of moisture. I watched as the deer dug through the snow in search of food. I listened to the calls of the coyotes singing in the silver moonlight of the freezing nights. And as the snowflakes, the deer and the coyotes touched my soul, I realized that a life may be taken, but no one can take the legacy and memories of that life. They can take my son, but they can't take my love for my son. They can take my land, but they can't take my love of the land. They can take my every possession, but they can't take the love in my soul.

"And it's the love inside of me that makes my heart dance. I don't need anything at all to be grateful for the experience of seeing the sun rise, witnessing the silence of the snow fall, listening to the serenade of the birds, watching the grace of the deer and feeling the warmth of embracing another soul.

"I've been reading and contemplating the words of Monsignor Romero again. His struggle was much more severe than mine, and he managed to be a beacon of light for millions of people."

After these words, David stayed silent for a while. I laid my head against his shoulder and stroked his hand. David had found his way to the light again. I so loved this man.

"Losing the farm made me hate everyone involved with Empuro," he said. "I hated them for selling the chemicals that killed my son. I hated them for killing Lee and the hundreds of thousands of farmers across the planet. I hated them for hijacking the ownership of seeds, of life itself. I hated them for their oppression of farmers in North America, and I hated them for stealing my land.

"But by talking with Father Jack, reading Romero and contemplating love, human love, divine love, unconditional love and the feelings of love, I asked myself this question: 'If I start hating those people who did those things to my family on behalf of Empuro, where would my hate end? And wouldn't my hate darken my heart like it did theirs? Wouldn't that be my ultimate defeat?'

"My son was full of love. Tom was caring, always put others first, had an ability to savor every moment without worry. He lived like that to his last breath. How could I let anyone take that from me? My son showed me the way. His life and death give me the strength to open my heart to all. I can love the men of Empuro; I empathize with them, feel the darkness of their de-spiritualized world, and pray for them that they might find their way to the light."

David was calm and at peace. I hadn't seen him like that since before the Cancun protests. He had settled west of Clearmont, Wyoming, on a small piece of land, and he had dreamed up a new vision. He had built a small but charming log cabin that was heated by a wood stove. The cabin consisted of one room with a bed in one corner and in the other a small kitchen—just a stove, fridge and sink. A natural fir table graced the center of the cabin, and a large screened room with a view of the creek provided shelter from the mosquitoes on warm summer evenings. The electricity for the cabin was provided by a micro-hydro turbine powered by the creek. David's water came from a spring that fed the creek. The cabin provided shelter and comfort for him and Jody.

Tessa had grown up and moved to Boston. She was accepted into the faculty of law at Harvard. I'm sure David's legal trouble with Empuro influenced her choice of study. She was going to make a great lawyer with a heart for social justice. The world was in need of many more of those people.

My visits to the Greens' had become less frequent. There was no need anymore to be a surrogate mother to Tessa. And the farm was now so small that David could care for everything, including Jody, without needing my help. I had accepted a project which required me to spend the winter in France.

Having returned, I was glad to see how well David was recovering from his loss. Whenever I visited now I stayed in David's parents' trailer, which functioned as the guest room.

I still tried to spend many weekends with them; after all, we had become part of each other's lives and it was difficult to change that. But the distance from my home and my work in Spearfish didn't make things easier on our relationship.

"I'm going to disentangle myself from this world and demonstrate how life can go on just fine without the need for any of those large corporations," he had said when he started to build his new home. "I'll grow my own food, provide for my own heat and power, get my own water, and trade with some locals so I can pay my property taxes and buy a few clothes."

"You should run permaculture workshops to teach people how to live locally, with and from the land," I suggested. Then I thought about our dependence on a vehicle in today's world, and I was sure David wasn't going to ride either of his two horses back and forth to town.

"You forgot that you need a car and have to buy gas," I joked.

"No, I didn't," he said. "I've found two old diesel trucks and am converting them to run on waste vegetable oil. I already talked to some restaurants and they're happy to donate their waste to me. Driving isn't going to cost me much anymore. And I'll drive a green truck."

"You won't see it when you park in the field," I teased him.

"You will see it; it's red, and it will have sunflowers growing from its tailpipe! It sure won't make much of a footprint in the field."

Besides the cabin, David had built two cold frames to extend the growing season. Over the spring and summer he grew a lush garden with a variety of vegetables, flowers and herbs. All his seeds were heirloom seeds and he joined a seed-saver community. He sold a variety of tomatoes and other vegetables at the local farmers' markets. His produce was mouth-watering.

"Many of my customers don't want to buy tomatoes in the store anymore. They all taste bland after they've eaten mine. Amazing how we ever bought into accepting an inferior product in terms of taste, allowing food corporations to control the industry, centralize production and transport their produce for larger distances.

"But times are changing. People are searching for quality food now. I've some twenty customers who've asked me if I can grow their tomatoes for next year. What's even better is that they're paying me upfront to do it. They call it "CSA." It stands for Community Supported Agriculture. Maybe there's a chance, after all, that people here will start appreciating farmers like they do in Cuba," he said, and I could see renewed hope flicker in his eyes.

Lisa Flann, Psychology Student.

"Why do you go to school?" David asked. "Why do you learn? Are you planning to go to university? If so, why? What do you search for in education?"

Silence engulfed the group. Parents, teachers, grandparents—all asked us questions about school or our plans for university. But it was always along the lines of, "What are you going to study? What did you learn today?" But David would do as he had done many times, and lead us to dig deeper. Why did we study?

"Because we have to?" someone said.

"So you wouldn't go to school if you didn't have to? Really?" David challenged. As usual we all hung out on the floor spread over some cushions; David was one of us, just an over-aged teenager, but with more wisdom. He never lectured, he never offered his wisdom, but led us to find it for ourselves. It was fun, it took some time, but it was like an exciting treasure hunt for some secretly guided insights to life. I guess that's why we all kept coming back, week after week. I even started to look forward to "David's night"; that's what we called it. We never told him though.

"Because it will provide us with better jobs," someone else said.

"Why do you want better jobs? What's a better job?"

As usual, answers mostly led to more questions as David took us down the rabbit hole into our souls.

"We study and want better jobs so we can be successful?"

"Why do you want to be successful, and what does that mean to you?"

"It means that we can make more money," one of the guys in the group said. I wasn't sure if that was what success meant to me though; boys always think of money first.

"To be respected," someone else said.

"To be able to take care of a family, have a nice house and pay for the university education of our children," another student pitched in.

"To travel and see the world," another answer came.

"So when I'm old and rich, I can still get some young chick," one of the boys joked.

"I would have gone to university when I had a chance, if I had only known," David laughed. "Let's change the question," he said, bringing us back on topic. "What causes you to be happy?"

"Winning a football game," one of the boys said, and the answers started flowing again.

"Someone's smile."

"Just being with my boyfriend."

"Being together with my family and celebrating Thanksgiving."

"The sunrise."

"A hike in the mountains."

"Being loved," I said.

"How much time do you spend in school studying to be successful?" David asked, changing the question again.

"Twelve years, ten months per year, seven hours a day. Lots of time," one of the guys said.

"And how much time do you spend in school or anywhere else studying how to love and be happy?" David asked.

In silence we digested the point he had made.

"None," said someone, to stress the absurdity of what we had just come to realize.

"Well, the focus of this program isn't to help you to achieve in life, but to let you discover how to love life and live love," David said.

He had told us earlier in the year about his time in El Salvador and how until this day the Archbishop of San Salvador had inspired him. Then David read Romero's words: "It will be so easy when in the intimacy of each family, boys and girls are educated not to have more but to be more; not to take but to give themselves fully to others. We should be educated to love. The family is nothing other than love, and love is giving, love is giving oneself to the well-being of all; it is to work for a common happiness."

Throughout the program we learned to embrace life and find our purpose inside of our souls. We didn't stay in the library; David took us to his farm. He let us discover the wonders of nature, of life itself. We observed the empty space within a seed. Then we planted a bean and upon germination watched how new life grew out of the empty center with the two lobes of the planted bean attached to the seedling and falling off after a few days. We planted sunflowers at his farm and harvested the seeds—and that's how he taught us the multiplication of the bread, by growing and sharing our seeds. He took us to the forest to an old-growth pine tree and said, "See how majestic this tree is? All that glory is contained within this seed." And in wonder we all watched the tiny pine seed in his hand.

On his farm we learned to milk his goat and learned how the animal fed on the weeds on his property and was a complementary grazer to his horses. We made cheese and discovered how the cheesemaker works together with natural bacteria to create a dairy product that has a longer shelf life than milk. He taught us to bake bread and we observed how the baker works together with the yeast to create the bread. He told us how he hunted and how the deer came to offer its life to feed his family. And as we listened and observed, our gratitude and appreciation for life grew and we learned to love life.

"To love life, we only have to open our eyes and hearts to the wonders that surround us," he said. "But to live love we have to make a conscious choice."

He brought us to an isolated spot in the Big Horn Mountains and told us to contemplate our purpose in life. We had to write down all the things we were really good at, the things we enjoyed in our core, the people and events that had crossed our path and the lessons we had learned from them. Then he asked us to think ahead to the end of our lives and write our own eulogy, the legacy we wanted to leave behind. No one mentioned "success" as part of it. David then asked us to connect the things we had listed in our eulogy with the things we were naturally gifted for and the teachings life had brought us; and all of us discovered some common thread. In some mysterious way, life's fabric was guiding us; we only had to open our eyes to the pattern.

"Along your journey through life, there will be setbacks, or that's how you will perceive them. But that perception is your judgment. It's a judgment that can trap you, imprison your love in the depths of your heart, like it has done with my dearest wife. If you can withhold judgment, you'll find that every experience, however hard, is an opportunity: a lesson, something you can learn and grow from. Just like the life of the deer ends to give me life, so will certain things in your life end to make space for other things to grow. We're not in control. Yes, remember that; you're never in control! But if you can approach life like the explorers who find enjoyment in endless discovery, you'll never lose your love of life which is essential to living a life of love."

"But what does it mean to live love?" someone asked.

"To be love is to become the music when you are dancing, to be the joy when you are laughing, to work in unison with the yeast and the flour when baking, and to become one when you're making love.

"To be love is to experience the loss of a loved one and be grateful for the life that crossed your path. To be love is to lose everything you have and be able to draw your power from the rising sun and the magnificence of creation. To be love is to be able to forgive and love your enemy and your friend. To be love is to seed what's in your soul, to care for what grows around you and brings happiness for all, and to receive whatever life has in store for you. To be love is to connect with everything that surrounds you, with God's creation and the spirit of the Creator that animates everything. To be love is to use our personal power and skills for the common good, for the good of our neighbor, human and non-human. To be love is to be your brother's keeper."

TIM BENNETT, FRIEND, BUSINESSMAN.

I saw David last in the summer of 2006, his last summer. Without that meeting I might have had trouble finding my own peace. For reasons I've never understood, it was important to me how David thought of me, and that summer, I was in need of a confession. Not to a priest, but to my friend; the one I had seen only once since high school, but with whom I had forged a bond through childhood that lasted for a lifetime.

I had to go through the effort of tracking him down. He had moved, which took me a bit by surprise as building an organic farm is a long-term endeavor. Luckily his parents still lived in the same place, and so I found David on a little acreage in Wyoming which he had turned into a one-acre farm.

With a childlike adoration for the wonders of nature he showed me the squashes, pumpkins and corn in his garden and the tomatoes in his cold frame.

While he cooked up some tender venison and prepared a fresh salad right from his garden, he told me about his legal fight with Empuro without showing any sign of regret or anger.

"I'm really sorry to hear what happened," I said.

"Yeah, I was sorry too," he said, "but life only delivers what we can handle. And if we roll with the punches there's always something new to discover, something to be grateful for."

I was astonished how David had been able to rise above the sorrow of loss. When we met in the Black Hills I had seen glimpses of anger that raged inside of him. For most people extra hardship lets them slip further down, but for David it had done the opposite. It had strengthened his ability to savor the intensity of every fleeting moment and be deeply grateful for the experience of being alive.

I was excited because I knew David would welcome my motivation for visiting him, and for the first time since high school I thought he would appreciate the choice I had made.

"I went through some changes myself," I said.

"Tell me about it," he said with eagerness in his voice and so I told him my story.

"A year ago, I was diagnosed with a rare tumor," I started. "They had to perform emergency surgery. The chances I was going to make it were slim to none. I was afraid, and suddenly felt so powerless, so out of control. I was used to being in control, running this world, being in charge. I was afraid not for me, but for what would happen to my children and my wife. I never told them the risk I was facing; I couldn't tell them. I knew I had a good insurance policy and so my wife would be financially well off if I died. I reasoned there was no point in worrying her in advance.

"But I couldn't save them from the pain if I were to die. I couldn't be there for the birthdays, for the weddings of my children, for the births of my grandchildren.

"They had to prepare me with medication for two weeks before the surgery. And with only fourteen more days to live I felt myself sink into the darkest corners of my soul. I worried every second of the day. And because of my worry, I didn't feel the loving caress of my wife or hear the words of kindness from my children.

"Then I thought of you, of how you were always able to enjoy the sunrise, and I realized that all my worry was preventing me from enjoying the moment. And for the first time since that day we plunged into the ocean at White Rock, I surrendered myself to life; I let go of the notions of security and control. I accepted whatever life had in store for me, and in that very instant all the color returned to it, and it was brighter than it had ever been during my adult life. I went into surgery prepared to leave this world.

"The doctors worked on me in the operating room for some thirteen hours, and lo and behold, when I opened my eyes, I was still here. I was given new life, a second chance.

"The day after the surgery they wanted me to get up and go to the bathroom. And then the most miraculous thing happened. I haven't told this to a lot of people, but I know you will understand. I was peeing, and all of a sudden I got nauseated. Before I could grab anything, I passed out and collapsed. I had fainted in the past, but this was different. Instead of the lights going out and turning back on when you become conscious again, I had a very surreal and lucid experience.

"I left my body and was part of the light of God. The feeling of peacefulness and love was overwhelming. What was most curious is that I wasn't just in the light; I was an intrinsic part of it, a part of the light source that was infused in every particle of the universe. I was connected to all of it, completely one with it, yet separate at the same time. I didn't want to leave. I could think about my wife and children, and I knew they would receive all the love they needed in their lives. And just then when I wanted to stay, I felt the connection fading, and the next thing I felt was a hard slap on my cheek by the nurse.

"When I regained consciousness, I found the entire experience was too surreal for me to comprehend. I had developed internal bleeding and collapsed in the bathroom. Two nurses dragged me out, only semi-conscious. At the time I was staying in a shared room, with three other guys who were recovering from surgery. And as the nurses dragged me to my bed, the guy across from me looked me in the eyes and said, 'You've been in the light!'"

"Later in the day, when the doctors had me stabilized and the critical period had passed, I needed to know if I had heard the man right.

"What did you say when they brought me back in the room?" I asked.

"You've been in the light!" he repeated.

I was astounded. "How did you know?" I asked.

"I could see it in your eyes."

"But how did you know about the light?" I asked.

"I've been there four times," he said. "I've been clinically dead four times, and each time I was in the light. I know where you've been."

The following day, they moved the man to another room. I've never seen him again, but I realize to this day that without that man, I might not have believed what I had experienced. It simply was too surreal, too intense, and beyond anything the mind can grasp.

"I'm glad you're here, still here. And I feel honored that you came to tell me your story," David said.

"I didn't just come to tell you my story," I said. "I came to tell you that you were right."

"You didn't have to come for that. I already knew that," he laughed.

"No, seriously. You were right about the system, about the futility of chasing digital numbers on a bank account, about spending a life climbing a corporate ladder when I could have used all that time to make a positive difference in this world. I came to tell you how I admire your resilience to stay the course, and how you've inspired me to do the same. I've quit my career as a banker. Not sure what I'm going to do yet—maybe I'll write a book—but whatever I do, it will be from my heart, driven by love, and I'm sure that will be more meaningful than real-life Monopoly can ever be."

We sat for a while in silence. Why did I feel uncomfortable to sit in stillness with most other people, but was totally at ease when it was with David?

"Being on borrowed time has helped me to prioritize," I said, breaking the quiet of the room. "I want to make every minute of life count. Life is precious, and none of us controls when it will end.

"It has also helped me see past some of my fears. I've seen where we're going, and it's an amazing place, so why worry about the time when we're asked to move from here to there; why worry about death?"

"This isn't an easy path you've chosen, Tim," David said. "You were at the top; maybe you could have made some changes from inside."

"Not in the current system," I said. "It's rigged right from the bottom up."

"What do you mean?"

"Did you ever question why people keep running on this treadmill? Spending their life on work they don't enjoy, laboring at several jobs just to make ends meet? Have you ever questioned why things are the way they are?"

"I ask myself this all the time. With what I learned from you last time, I realized that the corporate charter is a main reason, because it demands that the people who work for the company act in the short-term interest of the shareholders."

"There is another fundamental reason," I revealed. "One which, as a banker, I'm very familiar with. It has to do with the creation of money. That's how the bankers of this world keep the entire scam running and coerce people into economic slavery.

"If you live in a hunting or agricultural society, you spend your time each day providing for food, shelter and clothing, all of which can be obtained in exchange for labor and from the environment that surrounds you. You can trade, but the things you trade are always the product of your own labor and so there is always a fair exchange. Debt doesn't exist in such a society. And as you go about your work you're confronted at every moment with the wonders of nature.

"But in our current society, we've taken away people's access to land. In our society people can only buy food, shelter or clothing if they have access to money. As a result, those who control the money supply control the world. They define the game you need to play as well as the rules of that game. They define what you have to do to obtain that elusive money which you need in order to buy food, clothing and shelter.

"For almost a century now the bankers of this world have herded people towards the cities and taken control of an ever increasing number of assets in the world, simply by the way our system is designed. It all revolves around the way money is created in a private banking system. And even the Federal Reserve is a private bank.

"Money is being created when someone borrows money from a bank. At that point, the bank prints money by taking paper and coloring it with ink, or issuing some dollar digits on a computer. For providing that money they charge interest and register your debt. And here is where the problem lies. The interest has to be paid, of course, because that is how the private institution makes its profit, but no money was ever supplied into the market to be able to pay it."

"I don't understand," David said.

"Let me give you a small scale example," I said. "Let's have the total market consist of ten people and one private bank. In order to provide the market with money—notes that will facilitate trading—the bank lends one thousand dollars to each person. In other words, the bank creates a total of ten thousand dollars to circulate in the market. For this service the bank charges each person ten percent interest on their loan. So, it expects to receive eleven thousand dollars back. But only ten thousand dollars were issued, which makes it mathematically impossible for them to ever receive the interest. Do you see what I'm saying?"

"I think I do," David murmured.

"In reality it's a game of musical chairs since there's only enough money circulating in the market to pay the loan plus interest of nine people. By design the tenth person will default on the loan. The bank can never make any real profit in dollars since the maximum amount they can collect will always equal the amount they printed. The bank takes its profit when the tenth person defaults and they foreclose on the assets that are securing the loan."

"That's usury according to the Bible," David pondered out loud.

"It's a scam," I admitted. "It's much more complicated than what I just explained because due to the system of fractional banking, the banks don't even need to have the money they are lending anyone; they only need to have a reserve against that money. It's a large-scale swindle to keep people running on the treadmill, and the longer it goes on the more assets are being controlled by wealthy bankers and anonymous corporate shareholders.

"Not all interest is usury though, and not all interest creates this problem. When people pool their money together in credit unions and other forms of cooperatives, interest is floated back into the community because all money is public money instead of private. Such financial institutions are owned by the people and work for the people, and interest is simply a way to operate a system approved by the people and to the benefit of the people."

"So we would be better off banking with credit unions and banking co-ops," David said. "I always thought our government was issuing our money, not private bankers."

"Most people in America are under that impression. If we ever want to cure the boom and bust cycles of our economy, it is imperative that our governments issue their own money without interest that is siphoned off into the pockets of private bankers. The founding fathers were well aware of this. Jefferson said: 'If the American people ever allow private banks to control the issuance of their currency, first by inflation and then by deflation, the banks and corporations that will grow up around them will deprive the people of all their property until their children wake up homeless on the continent their fathers conquered. The issuing power of money should be taken from banks and restored to Congress and the people to whom it belongs. I sincerely believe the banking institutions having the issuing power of money are more dangerous to liberty than standing armies.'"

"How has the world come to this?" David questioned with sadness in his voice.

"Because too many people are like me, and not like you," I said. "I didn't take the time to question the rules or the purpose of the game—the game of business, the game we learn as children, the game we are taught so we can provide for ourselves and our families. When as a child I saw men in suits rise in status, I was intrigued and curious if I could play the game just as well. And I was good at the game, David. And the better I was playing this real-life monopoly game, the more people were pushed into poverty, the higher the environmental price, and the more money I made.

"As a people we behave like a mass of frogs that float in water with the temperature slowly rising. None will jump out until it's too late and the water boils. If the bankers of the world had tried to conquer this country, they would have failed, but they've taken their time and structured the system in such a way that warrants their desired outcome: control of the world's assets in the hands of a few while the masses are brainwashed to believe this is simply the way the world works."

"I invite you to become a member of the Gaia Confederation," David said after a period of silence. "I think your knowledge and insight will be valuable in creating a new design for the world."

David then told me about the secret society he was involved with, and for the first time since I had left my corporate life I had hope again. If more people were working towards establishing a true democratic society based on the values of freedom, equality and brotherhood, then there was hope for the world.

JOHN HOWARD, RETIRED FBI AGENT.

"What makes you think people have to be governed? Maybe it isn't the structure of the societies that was the cause of their demise, but simply the entire concept of governance. Do you see anything around you in nature that is governed?" the note read.

Can you imagine what would happen to people if they weren't governed? We would have all-out chaos. Looting and plundering in the streets. There would be no law and order. Imagine raising a family without security! But I kid you not, that was an actual message that we intercepted between members of the Gaia Confederation. These were the things they discussed in all seriousness.

People have been governed for over five thousand years. There's no civilization without some type of structure or government. Only primitive clans or tribes didn't have a government, and see where that left them. They never progressed; for tens of thousands of years they stayed mere savages. And even now that we have brought civilization to those people on a platter, we only have trouble with them. They just don't get it; they are unable to imagine a civilized life.

I never understood the logic of the second question. What did nature have to do with it? Why would it matter if anything else in nature is governed or not? We're talking about people here, not animals or plants. More sophisticated beings need more sophisticated structures; it's as simple as that. I tell you some of the things we intercepted were absolutely absurd!

If they hadn't started talking about uniting the citizen movements, we would have stopped spending any time on the Gaia Confederation. But whenever we hear uniting, that's a bad sign. The rule is "divide and conquer." It's been proven for thousands of years that the rulers who know how to apply that axiom maintain their power. But like with most of the other talk of the Gaia Confederation, I was convinced anything this movement discussed would remain just talk. They weren't practical people.

"Uniting in diversity." That's how they envisioned it. Now from where I stand, that means divided. It's just too easy to turn different groups of people against each other by focusing them on their differences. So again there didn't seem to be any real threat.

Over time the Gaia Confederation came to some consensus with regard to their vision. Everyone in the office agreed that it was just slightly utopian. It sounded a bit like the flower power movement of the sixties. And how long did that last, and what real changes did it bring forth in the world? I'm sure you get my point, and you will see similarities with the flower power movement in the four key pillars of the Gaia Confederation:

1. People united in diversity
2. Applied natural wisdom and natural laws
3. Small is beautiful
4. Love is supreme

The Confederation also talked about forgiveness of the superclass. Can you imagine? For what? For having brought us civilization, a house, a car and a television?

Once in a while there were some things that made us pay attention. Like, for instance, a communication from a Mexican member who wrote: "If all the civil groups around the world were to unite, campaign and organize national strikes to demand a change to the corporate charter we could make a quantum leap towards a sustainable world. By demanding that corporations are not considered legal persons with the same rights as natural persons, but rather legal institutions to serve a specific economic purpose, some of the legal absurdity of corporations using the laws made for people would cease to exist. And if the size of corporations were limited and their activity localized, trade would regain its entrepreneurship, creativity, fairness and freedom. Upon achievement of those things many of the issues the different civil movements are fighting against would dissolve."

Now that got our attention. Imagine if that were to happen; you've seen the chaos in Seattle with the WTO and at some of those other meetings. The good thing about those protests is their cooperation focuses each time on a single event and after that every civil group moves back onto their own specific agenda. So once the event is over, the world goes back to normal. But if they were to unite for a change in such a fundamental institution as the corporation, that could prove to be very dangerous.

Good thing the idea was shot down quickly by some Gaia members who were leaders of civil movements. They were quick to point out that their organizations were funded by large corporations and so they couldn't demand such a thing since that would cut off their funding. And who bites the hand that feeds him? Those in power are there for a reason, and they're not dumb. Every society has its troublemakers. So as long as you give them something to make trouble about—and even fund it—they're happy and won't consider doing real damage to the current status quo.

The other time we got concerned was when one of the Confederation members from an island group in the Pacific suggested it was the responsibility of the Gaia Confederation to protect Mother Earth and sustainable ways of life. In case a civil campaign failed due to a corrupt legal system that protects the rights of corporations instead of the true foundations for life, she suggested blowing up electricity towers, factories and other infrastructure that keeps this society in existence. We took that threat seriously. But the Confederation was policing itself quite well, and the majority always found ways to overrule the things that could tip the scale and threaten the world as we know it.

I had to grin about the great work our media has done in framing what's acceptable and what's not. I remember the first time I watched a news report on corporate sabotage. Someone had blown up a pipeline. It caused some corporate damage, although there wasn't any real threat to civilians. Yet as actions like this could endanger the stability of the world, on every channel the media echoed the words "eco-terrorism," and in no time that's how people referred to such actions, even though there was no terror element in it at all. You know the aim of terrorism is to create fear, to terrorize the masses. This was an act of sabotage with no element of terror at all, but I tell you, the term "eco-terrorism" made my life a lot easier.

A good example was the Gaia Confederation itself. The member that suggested sabotaging corporate infrastructure was immediately condemned by the rest of the group as an eco-terrorist, and it was made clear such violent action would only lead to more counter violence. They were probably right in that assessment.

When the member protested and suggested that inaction was much the same as being complicit to the destruction of earth and life itself, and therefore a violation of the supreme value of love, no answer came. He was deemed an eco-terrorist, and the subject wasn't worth any further attention. Do you see why we had never expected anything as violent as what David did?

In the last communication we intercepted from David, he told the members of the Confederation that he was working on a plan that would strike at the root of the current power structure.

We weren't quite sure what that was, but the man had no resources anymore, and most of his talk was about love and forgiveness, not about fighting or revenge. He had to make ends meet from a small piece of land with some kind of a vegetable garden. He even made his own electricity and drove his car on waste vegetable oil because he couldn't afford to buy power like most of us do. In one of his messages he called his way of life "permaculture." Nice word, but I just call it "poor."

So given the type of things we had seen of this organization, we didn't take David's plan very seriously. I guess we should have considered the fact that the Gaia Confederation was extremely secretive and that he had concealed his membership from everyone around him with exception of this Indian. Well, maybe one more. You see, we also knew that David had suckered one of his old school buddies into it. We're not quite sure when, but the man quit his high-level executive position at one of the major banks to become some type of aspiring writer. The Confederation must have had some real good system of brainwashing people, and David must have been a master at it. I guess with David's past history we should have known that he was angry at the world and therefore could explode. But he never showed any aggression, so we didn't consider that avenue.

SOARING EAGLE, LAKOTA ELDER.

"How do you connect a disconnected people?" David asked.

"Disconnected from what?" I asked.

"From the creation all around us," he said. "When Tim came to visit me and told me about his business and city life, it struck me how disconnected people in cities were from the wonders of creation. They live in a de-spiritualized world. Instead of tending plants, building their home, or hunting and receiving an offer of life, they rent out their time for money in the form of the jobs they perform. Then they take that money to a store to buy a piece of steak with no notion that this meat belonged to an animal that died in order to feed the person, with no knowledge of the circumstances in which the animal lived or died, and with no knowledge as to where the animal came from.

"It's the same with vegetables. Often children these days don't know whether tomatoes or peppers grow on trees or garden plants. They've never seen a seed germinate, or observed creation at work as an entire plant or tree grown from a tiny little seed. People don't know the sounds of the night, and are afraid of the forests as they've become alienated from their natural world and hide in concrete cities. In their economic globalized world everything must be quantifiable. If it isn't, it cannot be bought, and therefore is of no value and no importance.

"But how can you quantify the beauty of a rainbow? How can you quantify the love in your heart? How can you quantify the wonder of birth or the loss of life? How do you spiritualize the world of such people, if it only consists of straight lines, hard concrete, and dollar numbers?"

I pondered the question for a while.

"You told me once about your time in Cuba," I said. "It seems that the Cubans had solved that by encouraging people to grow at least some food on their balconies and roofs.

"I've read about movements in some cities to keep backyard chickens; that would be another example of how to reconnect people with their brother chickens who provide us with eggs. The growth of those community-supported agricultural programs you talked about brings people in contact with the farmers who provide their food, which develops an appreciation and direct connection with the land. I think the spiritualization of cities, the reconnection with the wonders of creation is already happening. What might have triggered it is the fast pace with which we are losing a lot of creation. But no matter how it's caused, it's happening, and that's what counts."

"I've noticed the changes in my students as they become aware of the daily miracles that happen all around us," David said in agreement. "I think you're right. If people start growing even a few herbs, tomatoes or any other vegetables from seed on their window sill or balcony and when they have the chance to keep some backyard chickens, they will not only discover the heartfelt gratitude and wonder for the food they'll grow, but they will also discover the superior quality of that food in comparison with what is available in stores. That in turn might fuel the citizens' movement that demands better quality, sustainably farmed food with higher nutrient value."

"We indigenous people have a deep understanding of the web of life because we don't think in linear ways. Earth isn't linear, and neither is time. For us, everything revolves around the circle, the Great Wheel of Life. The experience of life is the expansion of one single dot of energy. And as the Creator expands itself into this existence, all of us must choose a point in the circle of life. Each point is different; each point has a different experience and unique perspective. And each point has its antipode. For light there is dark, for good there is bad, for long there is short. In the end the circle will always be balanced in time and space, no matter which point we choose.

"We indigenous people have been taught to observe the cycle of life and the universe and to align our actions with it."

"Soaring Eagle," David said, "I don't want to sound offensive and neglect the suffering and wisdom of your people, but you have to realize that each time you say, 'we indigenous people,' you do two things. You marginalize yourself as a people and you exclude me. There are many people across the world who embrace the indigenous values and ways and who, just like you, want to nurture a stronger connection with the earth again. But as long as you keep identifying yourself as 'indigenous people' you separate yourself from all those people.

"If you simply were to say, 'we, the people,' it would be inclusive of me. Everyone can see your long gray braids and will always know your indigenous heritage; there's no reason to explicitly state it.

"People across the world are searching for spiritual leadership. Indigenous people across the world carry the inherent spiritual heritage that connects us all with the wisdoms and laws of Mother Nature. If you were to say, 'we, the people,' you could step into your power, lead us and help us all find our place in the larger web of life."

Later that year in the fall David and I went on a hunting trip in the Big Horn Mountains. It was something that had become an annual event. We camped northeast of Medicine Mountain. Straight west was the great Medicine Wheel, one of the sacred sites of my people. That fall, White Cloud had turned twelve and accompanied us.

It was our custom before heading out on the hunt to visit the Medicine Wheel. We offered tobacco, cleansed our spirits with sage, and prayed for strength, courage, protection and for being worthy to receive the sacrifice of life. Shooting a deer or elk wasn't taken lightly by any of us. The hunt was a sacred dance that wove the fates of hunter and prey together into one moment of metamorphosis when one life through death transforms into another.

We all hunted in the traditional way, with bow and arrow. However, David carried a long bow which he preferred over our Indian bows.

The first morning we set out to hunt for elk. I had found a spot high on the mountain overlooking two valleys which gave me good sight to spy any elk herds. David had taken White Cloud with him, and they were sitting in between a few trees in the valley close by the creek. I could see them both well from my vantage point.

This was White Cloud's first hunt, so David had placed the boy some ten large steps away from him. Just enough to have his own spot, but close enough to be able to protect him.

We didn't see any elk that morning. However, after patiently waiting for about two hours, a bull moose appeared. The animal was grazing at a safe distance from where David and White Cloud were hiding. After some twenty minutes it looked like the moose was leaving the area, but suddenly it turned around and headed straight for the trees. From high up I could see a pond on the other side of the trees and figured the moose was on his way for a drink. David and White Cloud were sitting right in its path.

The bull would encounter White Cloud first. It was mid-October, the rut was on, and the bulls would be aggressive. A dangerous situation was developing in the valley. Most people think bears or cougars are the threat in the wild, but a bull moose in the rut is one of the most dangerous animals, and is actually the biggest killer of hunters. I was too far away; there was nothing I could do from where I was sitting.

When the moose was fifty yards from the tree line, David stood up, waved his arms and shouted, "Hey, Moose, we're here; go away. This is our ground." He wanted to warn the moose in the hope of scaring it off. White Cloud also stood up and did the same thing. But the boy was ten yards closer to the bull. At any other time of the year this would have worked and the moose would have turned around and run away, but not during the rut.

The bull shook his head, his beard swung from left to right. It lowered its head and with deep threatening barks it resolutely walked straight towards White Cloud. I held my breath. The angry animal stopped twenty yards from the young boy, head low, ready to charge. I saw David draw his bow, but knew he had nothing to shoot at other than a big head and antlers facing him. Then the unthinkable happened. A loud and angry scream that contained all the madness of his life welled up from deep in David's gut, and he charged the bull, putting himself between the dangerous beast and the boy. Taken by surprise the colossal animal turned around and ran away into the meadow.

Relief flooded my body. But halfway down the field the bull changed his mind. It turned around, shook its head again and another baritone angry woof announced his resolute march towards the trees. This time he took three extra steps and stopped. Again, the head was low, the antlers forward. The beast took in David who was standing a mere seventeen yards in front of him with only two trees between them. David was ready to shoot, and this time he had a clear shot since the bull was angled away just enough to mortally wound him. But we weren't here to hunt for moose, and David had no license for one. And so the two were locked in a standoff—the man with sticks, his bow and arrow, facing down the massive bull moose. No one moved an inch. The entire universe had collapsed into this one scene where two opponents measure each other up before an attack. Time had come to a standstill. What must have been a few minutes felt like an hour.

Then the bull turned around and walked away grumpily in search of another source of water.

White Cloud ran to David and the two fell into an earnest embrace.

When we got back together, White Cloud ran up to me and shouted in excitement, "Grandfather, Uncle David saved my life. He charged a bull moose."

"I know; I saw it all. I think we should call him 'Charging Bull' from now on," I laughed in relief. "That was quite a crazy stunt."

"I didn't have much choice," David said. "If we had retreated, he would have charged. And if I had stayed where I was, a charge would most certainly have killed White Cloud. I only had one option. Charge!"

David stayed quiet for the rest of the day, but adrenaline had pumped White Cloud's energy. The boy had never talked so much in one day, "Uncle Charging Bull this, Uncle Charging Bull that."

"It's Uncle David," David corrected. But for that entire hunting trip, White Cloud called him "Charging Bull." It was a story White Cloud would tell many times over.

That night, David and I sat around the fire. White Cloud was sound asleep in the tent.

We stared into the orange embers while the heat stroked our eyes.

"Thank you, my friend, for saving my grandson's life. What you did took real courage."

"Oh, it's nothing, anyone would have done it," said David, trying to wave away the importance of the day's events.

"But it wasn't anyone who was there this morning, it was you. You didn't run, you didn't just watch. You acted bravely and saved a young man's life. Without your crazy charge, the bull would have killed him. Thank you for giving him the rest of his life."

Then the big strong hunter broke down. His chest heaved a few times before he was able to squash his emotions and get himself back together. "I wish I had been able to save the lives of two other young boys as well, but I can't tell you how grateful I am to have been given the chance to save White Cloud. I've finally done something worth living for."

He stayed quiet for a while. There was no reason for me to say anything. The fire was doing its work in guiding the man deep into his soul.

"What made the difference today is that I didn't think about what was the right or wrong thing to do. I didn't use my mind to consider my actions, my safety or the consequences of acting or not acting. I simply followed instinct. I was guided by my heart, connected to the moment, simply playing out the role I had to play, my verse in the poem of life. Ever since Tom's death I've prayed daily for a chance to make things up, for a chance to redeem myself and do something positive with my life. Today in the forest, God has answered my prayers . . . because I learned to take guidance from my heart instead of my mind."

In silence we sat by the fire. Each in our own way contemplated life and death, the events of the day, and our role in the great wheel of existence.

FATHER JACK MARSHAL, PASTOR.

I know this probably doesn't sound good with David being a killer and all that, but he helped me find my purpose again. David helped me to remember why I had entered the Church, why I wanted to serve God. I wanted to follow Jesus' path and spread His word in order to bring more love to the people and contribute to the making of a more socially just world.

I don't know what possessed him on that tragic day, and I still struggle to fit it together with the man I've known.

Two weeks before those events he came to confession. I'm bound by secrecy so I can't share anything he said, but I can tell you that he had moved to a point beyond judging. He had come to understand that the way the world had evolved was perfect because it was God's creation. He was following his heart and doing what God asked him to do to contribute to His creation.

He said to me, not in confession, but once during one of our philosophical conversations, "I'll leave the judging up to God. I'm only to do what I'm to do." And he was right; that's what Jesus taught us. It's a real challenge in today's world where there's so much judging going on. But David was living a non-judgmental life. He was looking at how life was presented to him and acting according to what his heart told him to do. That was his strength, and that's what allowed him to rise above the tragedies along his path.

The only other thing I can say about that confession is that I can assure you he had moved to a point of forgiveness and that the life and words of the Archbishop Romero had guided him in that.

I know they say David was evil. I say, something possessed him that day.

Maybe the evil of capitalism—which David resisted just like Romero did—spread to his heart in a failing moment. And I pray that one day this system will get eradicated; it's a real poison to the human soul.

I know you might be surprised by my saying this; after all what does a priest know about economics, and what does the Church have to do with such mundane things? But Romero was right; Christ's way of Love has to permeate all our society's systems and institutions if we are to walk along His path. And capitalism is radically evil. It is contrary to the common good, and Jesus said that all have an equal right to life and creation. Capitalism is the antithesis of love and compassion. It's an abusive system; self-indulgent, obscene and contrary to everything Christ stood for.

David shared with me some text that few economists tend to remember these days. Adam Smith, the great economist whose words capitalists fence with to defend their robbery of the world, wrote in *The Wealth of Nations*:

> The interests of the dealers, however, in any particular branch of trade or manufacturers, is always in some respects different from, and even opposite to, that of the public. To widen the market and narrow the competition, is always the interest of the dealers.
> ...The proposal of any new law or regulation of commerce which comes from this order, ought always to be listened to with great precaution, and ought never to be adopted till after long and carefully examined, not only with the most scrupulous, but with the most suspicious attention.
> ...It comes from an order of men, whose interest is never exactly the same as that of the public, who have generally an interest to deceive and even to

oppress the public, and who accordingly have, upon many occasions, both deceived and oppressed it.

This capitalist market system that's in place today is by design geared to concentrate land, money and power into the hands of a few. It's really no different from Communism, which did the same; it centralized power, also in the name of the people, just like we now say it benefits the freedom of the people. But why would we be surprised by that, since both systems were bankrolled by the same wealthy families in the U.S. and Europe at the beginning of the twentieth century? With Communism they made the mistake of forbidding religion, and you can never stop people searching for a connection with the Divine. The capitalists were smarter; they allowed religion, even abused it to justify their ways, but by design prevented the values of any religion to enter economic life. In other words, capitalism forbids religious people to walk their talk and follow the path of the living Christ.

They keep presenting to people as though there are only two options for a society to choose from; either you're a capitalist, or a communist. But what about humanism or love-ism? Surely we are intelligent enough to dream up an economic system that embraces the values Jesus and other religious figures taught us.

Capitalism rewards wealth with wealth through interest and profits. Instead we should focus on reaping the fruits of our labor in a fair way so that all of humanity can participate in a life of dignity. The collection of interest was termed "usury" in the olden days, and was condemned by the Church and by great philosophers like Thomas of Aquinas, Aristotle, Plato, Cicero and Seneca.

David attended my church every Sunday, and we often got together during weekday evenings and discussed over a glass of wine the tragic state of the world and the role of the Church in leading people back to a way of life that respects creation and chooses spirit, values and brotherhood over money. From our talks I found a renewed passion in leading my parish.

At the last service David attended I read from a text of Archbishop Romero: "A civilization of love that does not demand justice of people would not be a true civilization: it would not delineate genuine human relations. It is a caricature of love to try to cover over with alms what is lacking in justice, to patch over with an appearance of benevolence when social justice is missing. True love begins by demanding what is just in the relations of those who love."

I could feel the strength of those words and the strength of Romero's spirit, and I allowed him to continue to work through me. And so I added: "A civilization of love that does not demand respect for God's creation would not be a true civilization: it would not delineate genuine faith in the world which God has given us. It is a caricature of love to try to cover over with incomplete scientific theories what is lacking in creative power and faith, to patch over with an appearance of knowledge when environmental sustainability is missing. True love begins by demanding gratitude and respect in our relations with God's creation."

KRISTEN SMITH, ENVIRONMENTALIST.

"I'm going to take you to the Cypress Hills," David said with a secret, playful flicker in his eyes. "Just you and me; we're going on an adventure."

"Do I have a say?" I challenged.

"I talked to Jody," he said with a smile on his face.

I was confused. I knew she still talked to him when they were alone, and that at times they could have some real good conversations. She just refused to allow her heart to feel any happiness anymore. As a result she had no love to give.

"I talked to Jody about us," he elaborated.

"You did that years ago; she knows about our friendship and understands, you said."

"Yes, but I talked about our love."

I wasn't quite sure if I had heard and understood him correctly, and didn't want to get my hopes up. I had come to accept that our love would stay of a platonic nature forever. It had taken a long time for me to take comfort in that, and I didn't want to rekindle an old dream.

"She still loves me, but her love can't reach me anymore. It's trapped inside of her and she doesn't allow it to reach this world anymore. But she wants me to be happy.

"Jody told me how she appreciates everything you have done for us, and for the love you brought to our family at a time when hers was locked inside."

David paused, grabbed my shoulders with both hands and looked me in the eyes while love poured out of him. I couldn't speak; I was afraid of ruining things by saying anything. And I didn't want to let my mind drift to what we could have; it would only torture my heart.

"We spoke about the physical need for people to express their love. She wants us both to be happy and has given her blessing for us to express the passion that we have buried in the depths of our souls.

"We're going . . ."

But before he could say another word, I had wrapped my arms around him and kissed him. I had dreamed of this moment for thirteen years. All the waiting for this man was finally paying off. I wanted to feel his lips, exchange our essence, touch his soul. There was no need for words, and I couldn't care less where we were going. Being together; that's what I longed for and looked forward to. We could finally honor what was in our hearts by offering our bodies to each other and celebrate in ecstasy the love between us.

"We'll leave in two weeks," he said when our embrace relaxed a bit. "You'll have time to go home, finish off your project. I'll pick you up in the Black Hills on May twenty-fifth."

"Why wait two weeks?" I asked, eager for us to be together. But David, as the romantic, wanted to do things right. There was a special place in the Cypress Hills he wanted to take me to, he said.

The rest of that day we spent together walking along the creek behind his house. We saw several deer. The roads and fields around Clearmont were always crowded with deer and antelope, especially at twilight.

"The native people say deer represent gentleness. We have a lot of that virtue here in this area," he said.

His talk with Jody and the prospect of the two of us traveling together had energized him. In excitement he shared with me the solutions he had started to develop to move beyond the current culture of destruction. For the first time he talked to me about the work he had been doing as a member of the Gaia Confederation.

His ideas had been inspired by a Mayan shaman who had told the members that at the height of the Mayan culture people simply decided to walk away from the world they had created because it had enslaved their souls instead of liberating them. They had traded love for lust and giving for taking. They had traded honor for fame and kindness for decadence. They had traded freedom for servitude and gratitude for greed. In the end they returned to the jungle from which they had emerged when environmental pressures forced them to wake up from the illusion they'd created.

The Gaia Confederation would soon call on people from across the planet to walk away from capitalism and globalization and to reestablish the proven model of small-scale community and cooperation that has served humanity for tens of thousands of years. They would encourage people to disentangle themselves from the current system.

"You have to realize," David said, "that everyone who's employed by these greedy transnational corporations feeds the system that destroys the very foundations of life. In essence, they're killing the life and future of their own children.

"The economics of peace and love are based on community, cooperation and localization. They're about integrating democracy into the economy. You could call it 'democracism.' One person, one vote, instead of one dollar, one vote.

"We could transform to such a society if people were to support and start small, local businesses instead of feeling dependent on jobs in multinationals. Cooperatives also practice those values, and there're many cooperatives around the world that function successfully, fueled by the combined creativity and power of their people. Even today, one billion people around the world are involved in some type of cooperative. Cooperatives are about creating jobs and providing living wages, not about making outrageous profits and paying obscene salaries to a few on top of the pyramid. Cooperatives employ the model of the circle—the law of nature—instead of the model of the triangle—the power model created by man."

Seeing the man I loved, the man who had gone through so much hardship, the man who'd lost so much in his life, seeing him full of excitement and hope, made my heart sing. The butterflies that I had locked away were once again dancing in my belly.

"But before we go, I first have to execute the first action of the Gaia Confederation towards this new world. I've volunteered and it will come with a certain risk. But I cannot hide anymore; I cannot run away from my destiny anymore. I ran when I left little Raul behind when violence and war were erupting around him in El Salvador. I left him behind because I was afraid. It wasn't love that led me at that time, it was fear. Fear guided me, and to this day Raul's shadow haunts my soul. I know that I'll have to pay for my cowardice one day. We only follow Jesus' path, honor the creation, and live the words of any religion in the world when we follow the path of Love, when we listen to our hearts, when we are prepared to sacrifice our lives instead of betraying our souls.

"I will honor the deaths of Raul and Tom and will make a stand for the greater good. I will act with empathy, and I will act in the spirit of forgiveness like Monsignor Romero has taught me. And like him I will not stray, but act with determination and defend the wonder of life, no matter the risks, no matter the consequences."

We embraced each other passionately when I departed that day. His eyes once again had the bright sparkling love which I had seen before Tom died.

I left, floating and cherishing the thought of spending time together, this time truly like man and wife.

It may have been the last time I saw him, but David has my heart forever.

Then came the tragic day. No one phoned me with the news; I saw it on television.

I was having a coffee break with a friend between classes. Suddenly a picture of my father appeared on the voiceless television screens that decorate most restaurants and bars these days. My friend kept on talking. For her my father's picture was only one of thousands of impersonal images that she would be bombarded with before the day would end.

For me my world came to a standstill. The conversation blanked out. My father's picture was on television, and I didn't have to understand a word of what was being said to know something was wrong. Something was badly wrong. A ranch scene out west; lots of police; ambulances; bodies covered by white sheets followed by pictures of people. And the logo of Empuro, the corporation that had robbed us of our farm and had produced the chemicals that had killed my brother Tom.

My heart was racing. Something terrible had happened. Something had shattered my world . . . again.

I felt my throat close up. I remembered all too well how things had changed when my brother died. I was only nine. It was like a hand, a cruel hand, had reached inside of my chest and had torn a piece of my heart out. It was a raw pain, a pain that connected me to all my relatives, past and future. A soul pain; primal, all-immersing, and eternal. Time had come to a standstill; the world consisted of my dead brother and me. Me, who was left behind; me, who had to walk through life robbed too early of the company of my loving playmate and protector. And I had cried. I had cried, and cried again, tears of pain that wiped away any trace of my innocent joy and trust in life. Bad things happened, and no one could protect you.

"I need to go," was all I said to my friend as I left. I wanted to run home, but couldn't. A black shadow descended over me and sucked the air from my chest.

So, I walked as fast as I could. I had to phone my mother but wanted the privacy of my apartment. It was only a few minutes walk. My legs felt like lead. It was only a few blocks to my new home, yet it was the most arduous distance I had ever crossed. When I arrived I felt like I had run a marathon. I called my mother, but there was no answer. I switched on the television and the story hit me full force. Once again I felt the hand reach inside my chest and tear a piece of my heart out. My father had died.

I collapsed. My hands reached for my chest as if to protect my heart from further pain. The pain from my soul streamed relentlessly in salty tears from my eyes. I curled up on the floor and sobbed uncontrollably.

I phoned my mother. Once again, no answer, and I cried some more. In a blur the morning turned to afternoon. Endless waves of anguish washed over me, and in the moments between, I reached out to my vanished mother who was beyond my reach.

That afternoon, in a zombie-like state, shocked and in denial, I made my way to the airport. I was never lucky with standby tickets, but that evening as if by magic, I found a seat on the first flight west. I connected in Denver and even made it on the last connecting flight to Sheridan.

I found my mother home, alone on the bench by the creek under the weeping willow. Her only company was the surrounding darkness and the comforting trickling of the stream. She didn't say a word when I arrived. Not a tear on her face, she stared through the distant blackness of the night into a world only she could see.

She never spoke again, and passed her remaining days as a recluse in the little log cabin along the creek, tending Dad's organic vegetable garden—his living legacy—and canning the produce from it even if it was way too much for her.

The police interrogated me rudely for hours. No empathy for a killer's daughter. They kept asking me about some kind of an organization called the "Gaia Confederation" of which they claimed my father was a leader.

Why could they not accept that if you keep pushing a man over and over again, he can snap? There was no need for a terror conspiracy theory here. But of course they couldn't provide the truth as motive. When they finally concluded I couldn't help them, they handed me my father's possessions. I shivered when they handed me his bullet-ridden bloody clothes. I didn't want them. What were they thinking?

But there were two things I did take with me: the pictures of two young boys whose innocent eyes full of love still peered out from behind the bloodstains that now covered them.

Father Jack spoke kind words during the funeral, but no one in the community came. The church was empty, except for me, Mom, Kristen, Soaring Eagle, White Cloud, Father Jack and the coffin with the lifeless body of my daddy.

When I walked through Sheridan, the whispers followed me like dark ghosts who tried to suffocate my heart. I knew my father had done something horrible the moments before his death. But I loved him. I was sorry for all the families affected, but it was my father's death that I mourned. His actions didn't as much appall me as they confused me, since they didn't fit the man and father whom I had known.

And so the journey of my healing commenced by uncovering the hidden layers of my father's life. But as I learned more about him my confusion only increased. How could a man who so generously cared about people and the environment act so violently?

As I quilted the story of his life together, everything I heard convinced me that his time in El Salvador had marked his life. The ghost of Raul had never left him. He had tried to bury it, ignore the truth about the world we live in, a truth he had witnessed in a most devastating way, but when Tom died, Raul's ghost had come back in full force.

As a man who looked to address root causes, he patiently researched the systemic injustice of our culture. His goal was to strike the system at its core by providing a new way, a path based on love and kindness. He dreamed of shifting the balance in the world from greed to compassion, from destruction to sustainability, from brutality to social justice.

The image of the innocent young boy he abandoned when El Salvador was on the brink of civil war had haunted my father. It was clear that over the years he had accepted that he left Raul behind to die in a cruel war driven by the forces of greed. So I thought it was important to travel back to the time that scarred my father's soul.

And so I set out for El Salvador, to retrace my father's footsteps. I found myself wandering through the streets of San Salvador, trying to imagine the country during the late seventies and early eighties. Everywhere, the image of Monsignor Romero was plastered on the walls. His spirit was still alive among his people. There was still poverty and an extreme gap between the rich elite and the poor. There was democracy now, but only in politics, and just like at home the politics were controlled by those who ruled the economy. But at least the violence and oppression had stopped. I assumed the life circumstances of the poor had marginally improved, given the absence of protests or unrest like in my father's time.

But to what extent had democracy truly brought freedom? How can it bring freedom without redistribution of land and wealth? How can it even lead to freedom without providing a level economic playing field? Were the poor peasants truly better off and satisfied with the new government, or had they simply lost all hope after their rebellion was defeated by the El Salvador military with the help of mighty America? Did the people of the Land of the Free truly realize how their military was used to quench freedom in the rest of the world, all in the name of democracy, wealth and power, and the religion of greed? Did they realize how it was the source of their cheap coffee, clothes and consumer goods? How would they react if Monsignor Romero had addressed these words to them: "Charity for the poor without justice for the poor has little merit?"

My only reference point was the orphanage where my father had been a volunteer. I learned it had been bombed and burned down, but was then rebuilt by the church community. I ran into an old priest who remembered him.

"He was a good soul, your father," the priest said. "He genuinely cared; I could see it in his eyes. And he had a special place in his heart for a young boy who was brought to the orphanage with his two little sisters."

I was excited. This priest remembered my father and Raul. When he told me Raul was still alive, my heart skipped a beat and I couldn't hold back my tears. If only my father had known! He might have been able to forgive himself for leaving the young boy. It might have changed his life.

The priest promised to arrange for us to meet. I don't think I've ever been that nervous in my entire life. I was about to meet the ghost who had haunted my father's soul.

MEETING RAUL ESTEBAN, FARMER, EL SALVADOR.

"You are David's daughter?" Raul asked in disbelief when the priest had brought me to his home.

"How is David? Is he with you?"

I could see the excitement and hope rise in the now middle-aged man in anticipation of meeting my father again. His enthusiasm faded to disappointment, then sorrow, as he read the answer in my eyes.

"I'm afraid he passed on," I confirmed and wondered why it was easier for me to say it that way, as long as I didn't have to pronounce the word "dead."

Without hesitation, Raul stepped forward and wrapped his arms around me and I cried against his shoulder—the shoulder of the man who once found the same comfort in my father's lap. Here was a man I had never met before, and yet I felt his love and deep caring for my loss. As I did, I realized the bond that forms between people when they open their hearts to each other's pain, and how this, in its own way, gives birth to heartfelt love.

"He didn't have to be here. It wasn't his war, but he chose to be with us in the midst of all the danger and violence," Raul said when my tears had stopped flowing. "David, the gringo who was sent by God when my mother and father were taken away from us. He led me to realize that God would always be with us. He was an angel sent to me and my sisters in a time when we needed love, comfort and protection.

"He didn't have to face the injustice inflicted on our people; he could have stayed in his comfortable life in America. He didn't have to open his eyes to some forgotten peasants in El Salvador; he could have kept his eyes closed and stayed in his own world. He didn't have to open his heart and feel our pain; he could have ignored us and enjoyed the products of our suffering.

"I remember the day he left. I could see his struggle. When David left, I felt robbed again of a good soul who had taken care of me. Once more I had to face the world on my own. At least I was lucky to have my little sisters to care for. My mother had made me promise to look after them, so I didn't have much time to think about myself. But in the darkness of the night the shadows came in search of me, and it was then that I cried in silence. I cried for the loss of my mother, for the loss of my father, for the loss of David. I cried for being alone in the world, for feeling desperately helpless, and for having inherited the care of my little sisters before I had time to grow up. By morning, the light of the sun wiped away my tears and deep inside, every day, out of nowhere, I mustered up a smile for the care of my siblings.

"The orphanage was bombed. I don't know if the bombs belonged to the rebels or the military, and I don't care; it doesn't matter. Once again the world as I knew it was blown to pieces. And then, in between the rubble and smoke of the burning remnants of that world, another angel, a lost sixteen-year-old young woman, wandered listlessly through the rubble, crying,

abandoned by the world, abandoned by God. Her name was Leticia. She had lost her four little brothers and sisters in the attack.

"As if led by Divine guidance, she came to stand right in front of me while I was holding the hand of one of my sisters. I was trying to protect them. Not knowing what to do, I had closed my eyes and prayed to God for help. We didn't exchange a word, Leticia and I; we just stood there, looking each other in the eyes.

"I'll never forget that moment when God heard my prayers. I could see how Leticia's pain was pushed aside by a new sense of purpose, a new cause to live for. She held out her hand and I reached for it. She walked us out of the city into the country until we found an aunt of hers who sheltered us all. Leticia became my older sister. She cared for us like a mother. She never left us. We're still together. We're a close family, a family brought together by God.

"Over the years I came to understand that people are never permanently in our lives. They're only vehicles of God's love. And that love never abandons us. It simply takes different shapes in the forms of new people crossing our path.

"I was never angry with David for leaving us. He made a place for Leticia to come into our lives. I wished I could have told him how grateful I was for the love he gave me during my darkest days.

"You say he killed people, men that were believed to be responsible for the death of his son. Maybe he decided not to walk away anymore and take a stand and fight. There are times when we can ignore injustice and simply choose to create an alternative, a new world, choose not to participate in the unjust world. But there are other times when the unjust world will devour any attempt to ignore it, any attempt for a new creation, a new life. I've lived through such times here in El Salvador. In such times, the only option is fight or die. Maybe this time David chose to fight, to rise up and stop the injustice and clear the way for better things to grow."

Before I left, I handed Raul two pictures. The picture my dad had carried with him his entire life and which at one point graced the entrance of Crazy Horse Fields, and a picture of my father taken upon his return from El Salvador. And as though his fingers could touch my father's soul through time and space, Raul nostalgically stroked my father's image.

"I'll always remember him as the gringo angel sent by God to give me love during the darkest time of my life."

One day after I had returned from my trip to El Salvador and was visiting my mother, I searched my father's laptop for further clues. I came across an audio file entitled, "For Tessa." A file for me!

The preserved voice of my father confused me even more. It was dated the day before his death. I have posted it on my website. After all, he started this journey. He deserves the chance to explain things directly to you. The transcript follows:

TAPE TRANSCRIPT: MESSAGE FROM DAVID TO TESSA

May 16th, 2007.

My dearest Tessa, my daughter, my princess,

If you are listening to this message, then I am no more. I am so sorry that I won't see you graduate from university, that I won't be there when you marry and that I won't know your children. But please shed no tears. Don't cry over my death, but rather celebrate my life.

I didn't want to write you an explanation. I wanted you to hear it directly from me. Given the nature of my actions, there was no way I could talk to you about this in advance. So I left you this taped message in the hope that you'll find it.

Don't blame anyone for what's happened. The choice was mine. I made many mistakes in my life and paid for them dearly, I even paid for them with the life of your brother. I know I never brought that up with you, but the chemicals that Empuro produced couldn't have harmed your brother if I hadn't sprayed them on our fields.

What I've started now can change the world, and I finally feel I can make a difference.

I know my planned actions come with a risk—which is why I leave you this message—but they are my choice, they're from my heart. I've walked away from doing the right thing in the past from fear of getting in harm's way. But no more; I'm at peace with accepting the consequences of my actions. I hope with time you'll learn to understand and forgive me for leaving your life too early. But decisions of life and death don't belong to the realm of people. They are made by God. Our task is to use our lives wisely and contribute to His creation. Our task is to be grateful and find joy in daily miracles. Our task is to be the living love.

There was a time when my heart was full of rage. There was a time I wanted to shed blood because of hate. I went as far as tracking down the home of the CEO of Empuro, the man who headed the evil empire who made me kill my own son. I didn't care what would happen with my life; I wanted him to pay for everything he had destroyed. I drove to his home and arrived in the middle of the night. My rifle loaded, I waited till morning. I watched him leave his mansion. I was angry and ready to kill. But when I was about to aim and shoot, everything changed. Suddenly his son, a young boy about your brother's age at the time of his death, ran out of the house.

"Wait, Daddy, I'm coming," he shouted as he was still putting on his coat. When he reached his father, he looked up at him in admiration, and affectionately the father laid his hand on his son's shoulder. Then I realized that the killing had to end. There had to be another way. What difference would come out of the death of this one man? How would his son have felt if I had destroyed the life of his father on that day? There had to be a bigger plan, one that could be the catalyst for a new world to grow from.

I remembered how Monsignor Romero taught us that we all have a role in this world. And I remembered that I was a farmer. I grow things for the benefit of the people. I might plow a field, but only to seed and harvest.

Monsignor Romero showed us the power of forgiveness. It's time to forgive. It's time to unite. Corporate power is only paper power. It only has power if "we the People" give it power. Many of us work for the benefit of the few. But we have a choice. It may be time to stop being good citizens and return to being good humans; to act from the pureness of our hearts instead of from the darkness of our minds; to stop supporting a system that kills the lives of children, a system of living paper and dying hearts.

It's easy to pollute our hearts with anger and to hate the few. But we should remember they need our help to find the way. We see their wealth, glitter and power, but they're also people with sons and daughters, mothers and fathers, grandmothers and grandfathers, people with friends, people with dreams, goals and aspirations, people in search of happiness and love, and people who one day will die. And in the empty moment of death the only thing that will count is the legacy they left for the children. They will not be remembered for their money, possessions or buildings they created, but for the good they did to their fellow human beings. They will not be remembered for how high they soared in business but for their capacity to care for others. They will not be remembered for the success they achieved but for their love of life and their life of love.

So I decided to unite, instead of to fight. Let's unite people on the path of Love, behind what God showed us is good. My friend Soaring Eagle would say "Great Spirit," but in the end I don't think it matters to God what we call Him or Her, which lines we use to pray, which labels we boast or how we talk. What matters is how we are the living expression of Love. Sometimes that love is calm as a kitten at rest; at other times it's as ferocious as the cougar defending its young. Love can only be found in the present; fear stems from living in the future or the past. Love can have many forms, but it always comes from the heart.

In my life, I let two young boys down. But God gave me the chance to save another one. In the moment of saving White Cloud I learned to listen to my heart and offer my life to bring Love to this world.

It's time to make room for a new economy to grow, for a new society to take root—a society that's based on the economy of love. An economy that values life over money, an economy that serves the many instead of the few, an economy that is local instead of global, an economy that provides a living wage instead of maximum profit, an economy of cooperation instead of competition, an economy of Main Street instead of Wall Street, an economy of "we" instead of "me," an economy of living hearts and dying papers that benefits the children and doesn't rob them of life.

The solutions for such an economy are already everywhere around us in the form of credit unions, farmers' markets, permaculture, local living economies, farm-to-table and slow food movements, community-supported agriculture, seed savers and business cooperatives. The only thing that's required of us is to do our part; to become active, rise up and take control of our destiny.

But for new things to grow, old things have to go. Main Street doesn't need Wall Street. It's time to discard the illusion of paper power and recognize the true power of life. It's time to kill Wall Street.

I've been working in secret with a group of people from all across the planet for several years now to develop the basis for such a new society. When you listen to this tape, I will have paid with my life for my actions in bringing the Gaia Confederation out of the shadows. It was a sacrifice I was well prepared to make for the creation of a better world. Before I volunteered for this task I was well aware of the risks. When the status quo gets challenged in a very real way, there are bound to be consequences when the super-elite of the world defends its position. But it is of vital importance for the future of your children for the Gaia Confederation to take root among the masses. And so I ask you, my daughter, please pick up the torch where I faltered, pick up the torch where I fell, and let us together through time realize the dream of a society of Love.

I love you and will always be with you,

Dad

I loved my father. It was strange to hear his voice, and his message resonated deep within me and moved me. But it also confused me to no end. How could he talk with such conviction about forgiveness and a new society of love in light of his actions on that tragic day? Had he succumbed in the end to the evil of this world? Had he allowed the dark side of his heart to gain control? How could he expect me to commence building an organization drenched in blood?

I was left with more questions than answers. And for a year I tried to make sense of the senseless killing. I tried to understand what it meant to be a killer's daughter. And I tried to wash the blood from a noble vision.

One year to the day after my father was killed, my mother committed suicide. My father's death had sucked the last spark of life out of her. I found her on a little bench along the creek under the weeping willow. It was their favorite spot, and many nights they could be seen sitting there together in silence enjoying the twilight. "Listen to the voice of nature," my father would say. "It's always most alive at the time when light and darkness dance together in the twilight."

When I cleaned out the cabin along the creek, I let my memories drift on the items that took me back to my childhood. And it was only when I sat down on my parents' bed and started reading my mother's diary that I came to understand the love my father lived and the sacrifice he had made in its name.

DIARY OF JODY PALMER, DAVID'S WIFE.

May 18th, 2007.

Dear David, my love,

I hope you can forgive me for what I'm about to do. I, like no other, know the strength of your soul and the love of your heart.

I've seen how you found your inspiration in the life and death of our child; how you grew a vision from the smile of an innocent boy pure enough to inspire the entire world. I realize a better world needs to be founded on love and forgiveness. And even though I've tried for years, I cannot find it in my heart to forgive what they did to my little boy.

I've witnessed your struggle for years. I watched you fall down only to stand up again, over and over again in pursuit of your dream to grow a new and better society. I know you are a farmer; you grow things. And my impotence to help grow your dream saddened me further. Love and caring are needed to work towards a dream. But I have none to give. There is no love inside of me. There have been fleeting moments when light does well up from a source beyond me. But before it can reach the world outside of me, it gets swallowed up by the black hole in my heart, the hole of grief for the son we lost.

The pills you gave me on the doctor's advice kept me for years in a state of surreal living. Life to me was distant and unreal. It happened outside of me. I was merely a spectator of an unfolding story around me.

It was no different than watching a television movie. I went through the motions of being alive, but didn't participate in the creation of life. I could see your joy, but couldn't feel your joy. I could see your pain, but couldn't feel your pain. I could see your struggle, but couldn't feel your struggle. I could see your love, but couldn't feel your love.

So a week ago, I secretly stopped taking my pills. And for the first time in years I could feel my senses come alive. I could suddenly feel your joys and pain, your struggle and your love. And as my heart regained the capacity to feel, everything became clear. For the first time since our son's death I found a purpose again. I found a way to give even though I've nothing to give, but can only take. It's hard to do something good for the world when you can only take. But then I remembered your words, "For something to live, something always has to die. Space must be made for new growth to flourish. There's a time and place to destroy, and a time and place to create." It's a law of this universe. So for a new dream to grow, an old one has to go.

It's time for me to give you something in the only way I can, and that's by taking. I will decapitate the snake of evil today, the evil that prevents your dream from growing. And by taking something from this world that destroys more than it creates, I'll end up giving. These highly paid executives of Empuro don't care about life; they only destroy for their paper games and their illusionary world of power. It's time to destroy the lives of evil just like they destroyed mine when I lost my child at their hands.

When you read this I will be no more. But please try to understand and accept my last gift to you, the only gift I'm capable of giving. It's my gift to life, to this world and to children like our loving Tom. For it, I'll take away the lives of those men and women of greed, people who only take. I hope you understand and can find forgiveness in your heart—you, my husband, who I loved so much, but could give so little to.

Your eternal love,

Jody

May 18th, 2008.

Dear Tessa, my daughter,

I've waited a year for this moment. I'm not sure why. Maybe I wanted to leave this world on the same day your father died. Maybe I felt obliged to do what he told me to do; to sit by the creek and let the whispers of the water cleanse my heart and guide me to the world of color that was stolen from me years ago.

My heart died when Tom died. I wish I could have given you more—given you my love—but I had nothing to give. I know you carry the strength of love from your father, and so I ask you for forgiveness.

I still have the memory of our life before Tom's death; the laughter, the smiles and the loving. But it's only a memory, one I've held onto dearly as it was the only colorful thing in my life. Since Tom's death, I've lived life in a glass cocoon. I could see the world around me, I could hear and touch it, but I couldn't reach it . . . and neither could it reach my heart. Cut off from the world, my heart shriveled to something colorless, soundless, cold and hard. It belonged to the living dead.

The day your brother was taken away from me, I wanted to join the world of the dead. I wanted to end this life in which no sunlight shines on me, no person touches me, no voice is heard by me and no love reaches me.

But how could I take my life and leave you my daughter, and your father—my loving husband—to bear another death? So I tried to hold on. I decided to live on until the time came that neither one of you needed me.

Last year, I had chosen the day to leave this world. It was to be the day your father died. And today, I'll finish my journey and join your brother and your father in the realms of the dead.

Your father had a strength of spirit and a love of heart that I could only envy. In my attempts to find a way back to this world, a way that would bring love into my life, I read the words of Romero, who inspired your father and guided him through life. But I didn't have the strength your father had. I remembered Romero's love, but I also remembered his brutal death. I remembered Romero's capacity to forgive, but I also remembered the ruthless indifference of those in power. I remembered Romero's living church, but I also remembered the death squads of the night. I remembered Romero's calls for social justice, but I also remembered how he failed to stop the violence.

I've seen how you struggled over the past year to find peace with the actions of your father and the way he died. But let me tell you, your father was a good man with a loving heart. It was his love for me that buried the truth of that day. I didn't have the heart to tell you about the events of that day; I couldn't face you with the truth. But believe me when I say, your father never killed a soul.

I had chosen to leave this world with a gift of taking on that day. It was I who shot those people; it was I who decided to rid the world of this evil. I guess that made me a sinner, but I don't really care. Those people deserved to die.

I know I should not be saying such things. But they killed my son and I never found forgiveness in my heart. The people I killed were people just like me, with a colorless heart of stone, cold and calculated, incapable of true love. Someone had to stop them, and who better than a person whose heart is already dead?

I know the scriptures say, "Thou shall not kill." But when we see evil kill and destroy along its way and we only watch and let it happen, doesn't that make us an accomplice to the destruction and killing? Does our inaction not turn us into killers? I don't know the answers to those questions; in the end, it will be God who judges. I do know that on that day, for the first time since Tom's death, I felt alive, even though I only had the darkness in my heart as a guide.

I sneaked out of the house in the darkness of the early morning. I had left a letter for your father on the table and was ready to join the dead. I had taken the shotgun and binoculars. As I drove to the ranch where evil was conspiring, a deer ran through my headlights and I knew gentleness was on my side. I could feel Tom's presence and was looking forward to seeing him soon. I opened the car window to let the fresh breeze fly through my hair. The smell of the cool morning air stirred my soul. I had a meeting with death, but had never felt so alive.

When I got near to the ranch in the twilight of the morning, I parked the old truck off the road in the trees and in silence, like a hunter waiting for its prey, observed any motion on the ranch.

Between eight and eight-thirty a.m., eight men and women entered a building that was a fair distance away from the main ranch house. I guessed it to be a small conference cabin. I drove the truck right up to it, grabbed the gun and walked in. My heart was racing, my senses heightened, my resolve unwavering.

When I walked in with the shotgun loaded, no one said a word; there was no need. I could read fear and paralysis in the executives' eyes. Then I aimed and shot the man at the head of the table. The blood and dead body only fed my hatred and strengthened the paralyzed state of the others in the room. And I shot again, and again, and again.

When it was over, I walked among the dead bodies. I felt no remorse, but also no relief from the pain of the loss of my son. My heart was as cold as always, but I felt alive. Alive and capable of destroying evil; alive and aware of the accomplishment of my mission; alive and ready to join the dead.

And just when I was about to pull the trigger and leave for another world, David came running in. He must have woken up and found the scribbled note with the name of the ranch and the directions which I had carelessly left on the table.

The look of horror on his face has haunted me every second over the past year. As he stepped through the blood and over the dead bodies, his posture changed to one of deep empathy. When he reached me his eyes were full of love and compassion. He didn't say a word, but took me in a loving embrace which, for the first time since Tom's death, touched my soul.

Gently but determinedly, he took the shotgun from my hands and said, "You go home now, love. You go home and hold our daughter. Maybe I should have done this for you years ago. Maybe their punishment would have allowed your love to flow from your heart again. You go home now. I'll deal with this."

I felt shame, but I also felt love again. I pressed my husband against me now that my heart at last filled again with the warmth of love. I was terrified to lose once more what was stolen from me years ago.

"You go now," he repeated, and gently pushed me away. Before I walked through the door, I looked one more time in his eyes, and I saw only peace, acceptance, forgiveness and the purest love.

When I reached the gate of the ranch, I heard another shot, and with that sound the love in my heart was once again locked up.

I didn't look behind me. I didn't want to face the reality of my actions. I had lost the second man I cared for.

This time, I was to blame.

Over the past year, I sat on the bench by the creek as David had told me. I listened to the whispers of the water, but found no way out of the dark maze in my heart.

Maybe good and evil aren't about what we do in the world. Maybe good and evil are only found in the heart; maybe they are merely the reflection of a heart filled with love and light, or one that is absent of love; a heart lost in the dark dungeons of the mind.

WHITE CLOUD, 15, LAKOTA.

Every life is marked by certain events. Those events are engraved in our souls. Their memories don't fade, but they are alive and they feed us.

One of those days happened when I was seven. We returned home, late at night, to our trailer at the Pine Ridge Reservation. I was half asleep in the car. My mother stroked my hair to wake me up. My dad went ahead and walked through our yard to our home. Mom took me in her arms.

It was a dark night. A warm breeze kissed my cheeks and nudged me further out of my sleep. I smelled the lingering scent of sweetgrass and the smoke of fire in Mom's jacket. Dad opened the door to our trailer and turned on the light, and in the blink of an eye, our world changed forever. The trailer exploded and the raging flames took my daddy.

My mother cried for four days. I cried with her. Then she took my hand and said, "Now it's just the two of us. We will survive; we will walk on."

"But we have no home anymore, Mommy," I said.

"We will always have a home," she said. "Your home is in my heart and mine is in yours. As long as we have each other, we will have a home; we just don't have a house to put it in."

"I miss Daddy," I said.

"So do I."

We sat in silence, my head on her chest, and I listened to the soft beat of her heart, my home.

"The Creator works in mysterious ways but always looks after us," she said. "Daddy will never leave your heart, but he had to make space in your life for another soul to walk into our hearts. Pay attention; remember your father, but be grateful for what life offers you."

A year later Uncle David walked into my life, and he now lives on in my heart, just like my dad has kept on living there. Uncle David was a white man with a red heart. I've come to realize that it's not blood or color that determine kinship of the soul, but the love in a man's heart, the passion of his spirit and the gratitude with which he walks.

Uncle David took me with him into the hills, mountains and forest. He took me on a path that connected me with the land and spirits of my ancestors. He guided me in the sacred dance of the hunt. Uncle David was there when I received the sacrifice of my first deer; a life that feeds me; a life that now lives as part of me; a life that taught me to honor the union of the power of the bow and the focus of the arrow. I've come to respect the deer as my brother and Earth as my mother. And I will protect my brother and care for my mother.

Uncle David taught me that there's a time to live and a time to die. There's a time to give and a time to receive. There's a time to rest and a time to seed. There's a time to grow and a time to harvest.

There's a time to fight and there's a time to unite. There's a time to learn and a time to teach. There is a time to come and a time to go.

We must know: "What's our time?"

Retracing my father's steps has not only been a journey of discovery, but also of self-reflection and growth for my own soul. In his life and death, I've found purpose, and so I've picked up the torch of a fallen warrior, a warrior of love, a warrior of light. I invite you, now that you have witnessed my father's life, to ask yourself what kind of world you create today. Are you serving greed or love? Are you serving living paper or living hearts?

It's time to reawaken our dreams and talk to our family, friends and neighbors about the world we will create together. We the people hold the power. We the people are the power! Just like the quote engraved in my father's desk says: "A democracy's power isn't found in its institutions, rules or laws, but in the love and courage of its people."

My father was a good man. I am my father's daughter. I do not care for and will not weep over dying paper, but I will love and celebrate living hearts.

With love and gratitude,

Tessa Green
September 21st, 2010.

"*Dear brothers and sisters, you the economically powerful, at this moment it is probable that the threat of an agrarian reform creates discouragement, fear, and maybe hatred in you, and may even cause you to decide to oppose this reform by every means possible. Probably there are some that prefer to destroy everything, radically damaging the economy of the country rather than to share with those whose labor they have taken advantage of for many years.*

The Church, who has served you well, tells you today: this is the moment to reveal yourselves as generous Christians and love as Jesus has loved us, who being rich, made himself poor for our sake."

-Archbishop Oscar Romero

EPILOGUE

I'm picking up my father's torch and will finish the task that made him fear for his life. I gave it serious thought as I know my father was right—when you point to the underlying cause of society's problems, it comes with real risks. All leaders of major social justice movements in history have been assassinated. But now that I understand the vision my father had and the risk he was prepared to take, I'm picking up his torch and in doing so will honor his life and his death. And so with this writing I'm bringing the Gaia Confederation from the shadows of secrecy into the public forum.

But I need your help. I ask you to set up Gaia Confederation chapters in your community to discuss not only the social and environmental footprint your community has on the world, but also the power and creativity you have, together, to invoke the changes needed to create a legacy and a world we can proudly leave for our children. And I ask you to share ideas; to question not only the whats and hows, but also the whys; to debate solutions in public forums.

It's time for us people to take our power back from the fictional corporate institutions we've created for our benefit; they don't exist for our enslavement. It's time for us to discuss in our communities the foundations of our society and the social and environmental price that is being paid in communities around the world. It's time for us to enter into dialogue around solutions and transitions. It's time for us to stand up, apply our intelligence guided by our capacity for love and do what must be done: change the power and structure of today's corporation. We have to redesign our economy so it cherishes the power of entrepreneurial freedom without enslaving our brothers and destroying the environment of our neighbors.

And so I invite you to join me. Don't let my father's life be in vain. Don't let my brother's life be in vain. Don't let the lives of all who suffered and died at the hands of corporate tyranny be in vain. Let us all be tiny raindrops of change and together form a mighty ocean of change. Let us form a tidal wave that wipes things clean so new seeds can grow. Together, let us transform a society of living paper into a society of living hearts and inspiring love.

Tessa Green

March 21st, 2011

AFTERWORD

While all characters and institutions in this book are fictitious and none of the events played out in any of the places described, stories like this play out each day the world over. *A People's Power* is a work of fiction but the events that affect David Green in this story are inspired by actual events. My purpose in writing this novel is not to sell certain ideas or perspectives, but rather to make you think about the world we are creating together, and to awaken the power within you to do what must be done for the children.

In case you want to research some of the topics the book touches on, you can find a recommended reading list and websites on related material at the **www.apeoplespower.com**.

I thank you for the time you've invested on this journey through David Green's life and hope you consider it time well spent.

Hugo Bonjean

For Educators and Book Clubs

Book clubs and educators enjoy Hugo's stories because they challenge the reader to think beyond the obvious and the status quo, they allow the reader to explore current issues that relate to inequality, democracy and economics in an entertaining and thought provoking way, and they always inspire and empower the reader to reach deep within and live a life of purpose.

When his schedule permits, Hugo presents at high schools, colleges, universities and conferences. From time to time Hugo also meets with book clubs in person or via Skype.

To request a book club visit, write an email to **bookclub@hugobonjean.com** and mark clearly in the subject line "Book club visit" and add the date and location to it.

For school, college or university presentations or conferences email **presentations@hugobonjean.com**.

Educators and book clubs can find questions to spark a discussion around the themes of *A People's Power* at the book's website:

www.apeoplespower.com

You can also provide your feedback there, suggest extra questions and provide any other book club or educational tips.

ACKNOWLEDGMENTS

I'm not sure where stories come from. Stephen King once wrote that as an author he was only the first reader. I couldn't agree more. Stories have a life of their own; the writer is merely the messenger; the first reader. And so I must first thank the muse for the journey she led me on. She led me to face the ugliness, injustice and cruelty of our current society, she led me to see the flaws in the foundation of our culture, she led me to experience a state of depression, and she led me to find inspiration and hope in our capacity for love.

But while the muse was leading, it was people who through their words and actions allowed me to take this journey. Many of them don't even know me, like the many authors whose work inspired this novel. Many others were unaware how an ordinary action or a simple word would inspire a twist or turn in the story.

Without taking away from the gratitude I extend to all those people, I want to make special mention of some.

My friend and missionary, Filip Croomheecke, shared with me during his visit last year how he found inspiration for his work in the life and words of Archbishop Romero. I remembered writing an essay in high school about the civil war in El Salvador and how shocked I was when Romero was assassinated, but I had never read any of Romero's speeches. Without Filip pointing me to Romero, this book would never have been written, as I hadn't been able to find inspiration to escape the depression I encountered in facing the doom and gloom of our world. Thank you, Filip. Thank you, Oscar Romero.

I want to express my appreciation to David Korten, Maude Barlow, Vandana Shiva, Diane Dreher, and to all the readers who have sent me encouraging emails after reading my previous books. Without such support, there wouldn't have been a third book.

I thank Colton for his picture of "a kiss in time" to his mother.

Colton's mom, Meara McIntosh, my mother, Betty Bonjean, and Patty Lowe helped me to understand the pain of a mother's grieving heart. I thank them for sharing those very personal experiences.

I thank Ed Iron Cloud and all the members of the Knife Chief Tiyospaye of the Oglala Lakota Tribe for giving me a glimpse into the life on the Pine Ridge Reservation, for taking me and my son on a buffalo kill and for letting us witness the strength of the native spirit and the important work of the Wakanyeja Pawicayapi organization in revitalizing families by returning to the fundamental Lakota virtues.

I thank Dahl McLean and his wife Talli, Carol LeResche, and Ann Loretan not only for opening up their farms and sharing some of their knowledge and stories, but also for inspiring me to restart and expand my own garden with heirloom seeds.

I express my gratitude to Alvin Manitopyes, a Cree elder, for opening up his sweat lodge to people of all backgrounds, for his prayers and for his spiritual guidance.

I thank Harold "Bud" Kary for sharing all the stories of the days his family settled in our valley and for his passionate rants in comparing those days with the consumption lifestyle of today.

My research would have taken much longer if it weren't for all the blogging and forums on the worldwide web. I'm grateful to all those who've shared experiences online. They allowed me to add color and detail to many parts of the story, like the pregnancy test, the heart breaking leukemia experience and the WTO protests in Cancun.

I am in awe of all who work tirelessly to change our current society into one that is based on love, and of farmers around the world who provide us with our food. They are my inspiration.

I thank my children, Bjorn, Fabian and Amber for putting up with a father who refuses to conform with the consumption society even though today's culture teaches them that money rules.

Then there is the great team working for Eagle Vision Publishing. Without their help it would be impossible for me to present such a well-polished story in such a professional manner. Editors Elizabeth Zack and Paula Kroeker made sure that my non-native English reads smoothly and that there are no loose ends in the story. A volunteer line edit team caught the last spelling and grammar errors; my thanks for this goes to Melaine Sax, Jill Dakers, John Robertson, Anthony Kroeker, and Rick Charlton (for his editing and help with the cover picture). I thank Monica Heincke for her translations of some of Oscar Romero's homilies. As always, Suzanne Oel did a superb job with the cover design, and covers do sell books.

I also thank all community members, who helped in some small or more substantial way, for their support.

And last but not least I thank my lovely wife, Ilse. She is the sun, the moon and the color in my life. Her relentless support allows my writing career to exist. Thanks to her love I can follow my dreams and be the man I am today.

HAVE YOU READ?

In the Eyes of Anahita

Paul, a successful business executive, gets confronted by his seven-year-old son with the question: "Dad, why do people have to pay for food?" When he realizes his son questions why, in our civilized society, we allow hunger to exist, he fails to produce an answer. During Paul's next business trip to South America, where he deals with some of the richest people on the continent, the question haunts him as he opens his eyes, heart and mind to the poverty around him. When he intends to help a begging grandmother in Argentina, he is dragged into a mysterious sequence of events during which he has to solve the riddle, "Are human beings being human?"

In the Eyes of Anahita is a captivating read that presents profound truth in the entertaining guise of fiction. Hugo Bonjean shares the story of a vision quest in the tradition of James Redfield's *Celestine Prophecy* and Daniel Quinn's *Ishmael*, but with deeper practical and spiritual insights. Highly recommended."

–Dr. David C. Korten, international bestselling author of *When Corporations Rule the World*.

HAVE YOU READ?

Seeds ... of Germination ... or Termination

The American Confederacy.

Nayla, a top scientist and respected board member of the mighty Carsanto Corporation, becomes the country's most wanted fugitive when she impulsively steals the company's only germinator seeds to protect the planet and her daughter's future. The

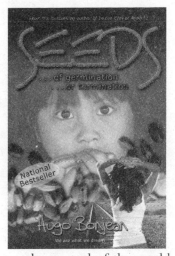

act endangers Carsanto's malicious plan to take control of the world through genetically modified terminator seeds. With Carsanto's ruthless security officer in hot pursuit, Nayla flees to the United Canadian Communities where a solitary mountain trapper guides her on a soul-searching adventure as they strive to bring the seeds to safety. Will she be able to rise to her true potential, save her daughter and allow the seeds of life to germinate on Earth?

". . . . a wake up call from the future – to make the choices today that will defend our freedoms tomorrow."

–Dr. Vandana Shiva, activist and author.

"If anyone thinks this is far-fetched ask the small farmers and peasants who controls their lives and crops today." –Maude Barlow, Chair, Council of Canadians

Our Commitment to a Sustainable World

This book is printed on Rolland Enviro 100 paper, made with 100% post-consumer waste, processed chlorine-free. For each 1,000 books of this title printed on this environmentally-friendly paper, the following resources are saved:

12 fully grown trees
8,554 gallons of water
1,082 pounds of solid waste
2.811 pounds of greenhouse gases
These numbers were determined using the eco-calculator of the Cascades Fine Paper Group (www.environmentalbychoice.com).

Traditionally the paper industry has been structured around wood as the source of fiber. According to the Worldwatch Institute, over 40 percent of the world's industrial wood harvest is used for the manufacture of paper. This has resulted in the decimation of our old growth forests, which continue to be clear-cut to make paper.

We honor paper and printing companies as well as retailers that are committed to introducing environmentally-friendly paper at competitive prices to the book industry, while at the same time diverting waste from landfills and addressing pollution issues. May many follow this responsible path!

ABOUT THE AUTHOR

Hugo Bonjean was born in Antwerp, Belgium. As a critical thinker with a strong sense for humanitarian issues and justice, he decided to study Social and Political Sciences at the University of Louvain. However, when he realized that a world revolving around money could only become sustainable through understanding and adjusting its driving economics, he changed direction and graduated in Antwerp with a B.S. in Accounting, thereafter completing his M.B.A. at the European University. After a few accounting jobs in the manufacturing industry, he joined Holiday Inn in a strategic development role. This was the beginning of a fast-paced twelve-year career that took Hugo all over the world.

When Marriott International appointed Hugo to the position of Vice President of Operations & Development for one of their divisions in Latin America, his firsthand experiences with poverty there rekindled the humanitarian values of his teens. After two years in this role he decided to dedicate the rest of his life to help shift the world towards sustainable models of living—economical, political, social, environmental and spiritual.

When his first book, *In the Eyes of Anahita*, made a life-changing impact on many readers, he became aware of the power of storytelling and he is now using that vehicle to engage people in social and environmental action.

Hugo practices permaculture and through his charity and non-profit work attempts to improve the life circumstances of struggling farmers in different parts of the world. Hugo lives with his family in the Rocky Mountain foothills near Calgary, Canada. He recharges his batteries while riding his horse in the backcountry.

CONTACT INFORMATION

Hugo always welcomes comments from his readers. You can send your feedback to:

info@hugobonjean.com

Take Action! Get further inspired, choose a cause, find volunteer positions and learn about Hugo's other involvements, his events, recommended reading list and speaking services at:

www.hugobonjean.com

Read material that was cut from this story, browse the author's research material for the book, listen to the recording left by David Green for his daughter Tessa and recommend the book trailer to others by visiting and directing your friends to:

www.apeoplespower.com

Check out Hugo's other books at:

www.intheeyesofanahita.com
www.seedsofgerminationortermination.com

You can also stay in touch with Hugo via Facebook.

From the Foreword: you can find out more about Julie Rempel and Fresh Air Flavours at: **www.freshairflavours.com**